A DESIGNER'S NOTEBOOK

McKnight & McKnight Publishing Company • Bloomington, Illinois

A DESIGNER'S NOTEBOOK

ARTHUR D. ANDERSON • LIVONIA PUBLIC SCHOOLS • LIVONIA, MICHIGAN

Part-Time Staff Member Eastern Michigan University • Wayne State University

Michigan State University

PREFACE

As part of your industrial arts work, you will have the responsibility for the "look" of your projects. Yours will be the thrill of designing beauty and utility into the objects you will make. This should be a challenge, for it is an opportunity to demonstrate to yourself and others the abilities you have to design and construct.

The problems and designing information presented in this book should serve only as a guide for your individual and group projects. Your teacher, your fellow students and your parents may be able to offer helpful suggestions as you plan the design and construction of your problem solution. Sincere research, planning, sketching, and experimentation will help you in your work. Remember that you are not asked to apply superficial surface ornamentation, but rather to develop a form of beauty suited to a purpose. A simple solution to a problem usually will be the best solution.

Arthur D. Anderson

TO BONNIE, JON, SUSAN AND ERIC

CONTENTS

INTRODUCTION

The chapters of this book are arranged by areas of design, woodworking, plastics, drafting and metalworking. The suggested problems and design information and designing techniques can be adapted to beginning as well as advanced problem solving experiences.

Each chapter relates to the next because of logical related processes and designing information. Design information is presented in the first chapter, for this is the foundation for all two- and three-dimensional planning. This is followed by wood sculpturing because of the definite trend toward the "sculptured look" of today's industrial products. Also, wood sculpturing is a grass roots approach to woodworking and gives an understanding of the structure and grain of wood. The reverse of sculpturing is lamination, which gives a concept of shaping and forming wood by utilizing its flexibility in thin sections.

The problem information is presented in this order in each chapter:
1. Suggested problems—simple and complex
2. Design information
3. Process information
4. Core problem
5. Variations of the core problem
6. Fabrication information
7. Other solutions to the problem
8. Experimentation

Problem ideas, design information, process information and suggestions for experimentation will offer a variety of avenues to an understanding of the potentials of industrial problems.

Arthur D. Anderson

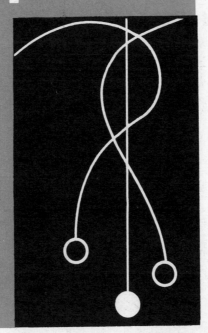

CHAPTER 1

DESIGN

design and you

In his research and planning to solve a design problem, the designer must consider the physical properties of materials, process information, material texture and color, etc. He must bring all of these together into a harmonious whole so that the end product is functional, attractive, and can be made efficiently and economically.

Your projects in industrial arts reflect something of yourself; therefore, they should apply the elements and principles of design. The more you become aware of and understand these elements and principles and apply them in the design of your projects, the better those end products will be. It will take a sincere effort on your part to apply the information presented in this chapter.

design continuum

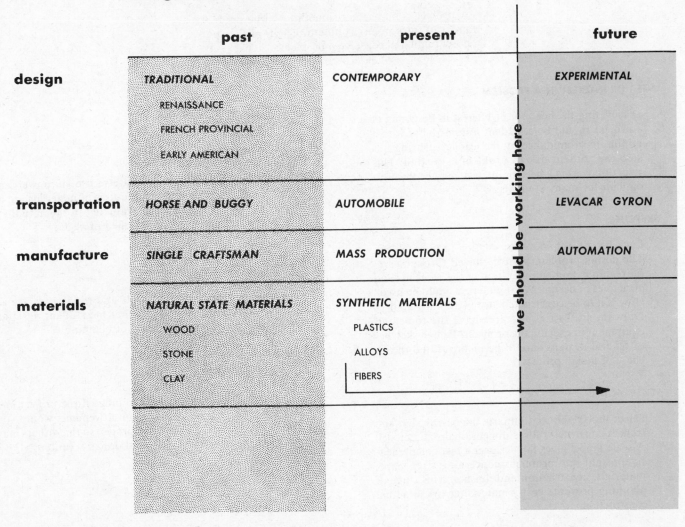

	past	present	future
design	TRADITIONAL RENAISSANCE FRENCH PROVINCIAL EARLY AMERICAN	CONTEMPORARY	EXPERIMENTAL
transportation	HORSE AND BUGGY	AUTOMOBILE	LEVACAR GYRON
manufacture	SINGLE CRAFTSMAN	MASS PRODUCTION	AUTOMATION
materials	NATURAL STATE MATERIALS WOOD STONE CLAY	SYNTHETIC MATERIALS PLASTICS ALLOYS FIBERS	

we should be working here

•——the design process——•

A project is more than something to be made. It must fit into an environment, accomplish a purpose, fulfill a need, solve a problem.

NEED OR INTEREST IN A PROBLEM

Discovering the need for or interest in designing of a project should be a student responsibility with a minimum of guidance by the teacher. During this step the student design problem is created. This step, discovering a need or interest, may be the most difficult for many students.

SKETCHES

Look for a fresh and valid solution to the problem. The design problem must be solved through careful planning and consideration of the elements and principles of design. What materials could be used? How is it to be constructed? Is it within my ability? Does the industrial arts area have the tools and equipment to execute the problem? Rough sketches of several designs should be incorporated in this phase of design process.

SCALE MODEL

Select the sketch that imparts the best design and from it construct a three dimensional scale model. A scale model gives the designer a fast comprehensive insight into problems concerning size, shape, materials, construction and finishes. This stage of planning prevents costly material errors in actual construction.

CONSTRUCTION

Accepted practices of safety, use of power and hand tools, equipment and uses of materials are all explored, studied and evaluated in the actual execution of a student designed project.

DRAWING

Work drawings, pictorials and renderings are all positive proof to others that the student designer has considered all phases of planning.

EVALUATION

This should be the time to judge if the project met the original needs. What improvements would you incorporate? Display the project so that others may see and evaluate your final design solution.

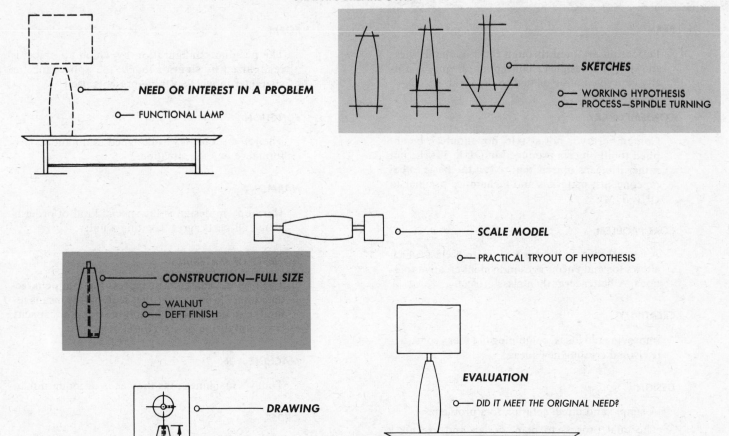

total problem involvement

GRAPHIC BREAKDOWN

NEED OR INTEREST IN A PROBLEM
○— FUNCTIONAL LAMP

SKETCHES
○— WORKING HYPOTHESIS
○— PROCESS—SPINDLE TURNING

SCALE MODEL
○— PRACTICAL TRYOUT OF HYPOTHESIS

CONSTRUCTION—FULL SIZE
○— WALNUT
○— DEFT FINISH

DRAWING
○— REFINEMENT OF HYPOTHESIS

EVALUATION
○— DID IT MEET THE ORIGINAL NEED?

●— spindle turning problem

●— design process —●

design and technical terms

BEAUTY

Perfection attained through form as the flawless showing of a designer's conception. Beauty is usually conceived of as related to the ideal.

CONTEMPORARY

Contemporary is not a style, nor should it be applied to all objects produced in OUR TIME; but rather it means objects that reflect the basic esthetic concepts, materials and techniques peculiar to OUR TIME.

CORE PROBLEM

A central idea or direction given to a class which allows for and encourages individual creative solutions. A better term than class project.

CREATIVITY

Improving old ideas, combining old ideas constructively and creating new ideas.

DESIGN

A simple and direct solution to a problem.
The total process to plan, design and execute a problem.

ECONOMY

Economy is the creation of harmony in design by the fewest and simplest means.

FORM

The peculiar configuration by which an object is recognized by sight or touch, the appearance or character in which a thing presents itself.

FUNCTION

The job a problem was designed to do and its performance in a use situation.

HARMONY

Harmony in design is the special kind of order in which all parts agree, creating a unity.

HONESTY OF MATERIALS

The use of a material to express the main characteristics and function of that material. It means using the material to its optimum strength, capacity and capitalizing on its natural color.

MACHINE AGE

Today's machines plus the needs of modern man.

ORDER

Order is the methodic disposition of elements according to a definite system.

PLAN

The steps of fabrication in logical order.

PRACTICAL DESIGN

A design approach used in engineering, architecture, industrial design and industrial arts.

SENSITIVITY

Quality or state of being sensitive to relationships; for example, the thickness of materials as they relate to a function.

SIMPLICITY

Materials are worked and assembled to satisfy functional and esthetic demands and are not complicated for the sake of difference or tool exercises.

SPIRIT OF OUR TIMES

Social changes brought about by mechanization and the introduction of new materials and production techniques are creating new forms for old things as well as new objects which have no counterparts in the past.

STRUCTURE

The working parts of a product that support, tie together, span, compress, etc., and which should be expressed by the shape of the product.

SURFACE DECORATION

Ornamentation is frequently used in an effort to beautify a project that is poor in design. For example, artificial hammer markings are frequently used to create texture on metal problems to disguise poor structural lines.

TECHNIQUE

A particular group of operations involving a certain material or materials which results in a completed problem. A better term than process.

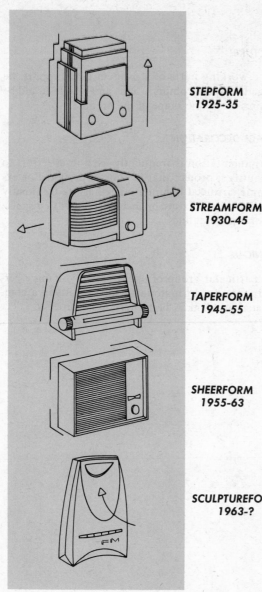

the five eras of styling

**STEPFORM
1925-35**

Best in architecture (often called the "skyscraper")
Vertical not horizontal accent
Steps, reeding and fluting
Lighting symbol

**STREAMFORM
1930-45**

Mystic Three (three parallel stripes appeared every-where).
The "Air Flow" Chrysler; 1934 marked the first move toward aerodynamic design of mass-produced cars. An excellent automobile, rejected by an unsophisticated public.
First use of aerodynamics
First time that industrial designers captured public imagination.

Streamlining
Horizontal accent
Louvers and stripes
Ball corners

**TAPERFORM
1945-55**

Trapezoidal block forms
Initiated the shift to crisp form
Crosshatching
Two-toning color
Still seen

**SHEERFORM
1955-63**

The "Square Look"
First appeared in the appliance industry
Pure at first but now lost
"Bow-Tie"

**SCULPTUREFORM
1963-?**

Starting to appear in architecture and transportation
Now appear as only detail on SHEERFORM

**in our industrial design age
styling clichés**

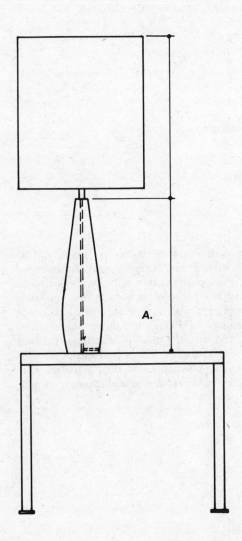
A.

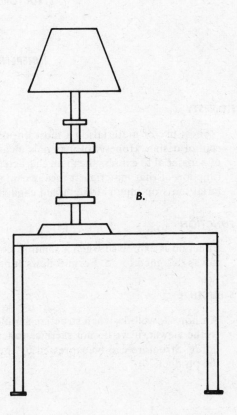

B.

9

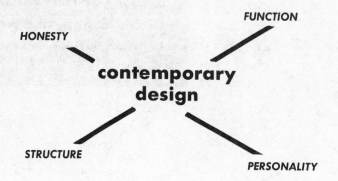

HONESTY

FUNCTION

contemporary design

STRUCTURE

PERSONALITY

INHERENT PROPERTIES OF CONTEMPORARY DESIGN

HONESTY

Honest use of materials is a most important precept of design. Honesty of materials means the use of a material to express the main characteristics and function of that material. It means using that material to its optimum strength and capacity.

FUNCTION

Function is expressed when a solution does the job it was designed to do. Form follows function.

STRUCTURE

An honest, well-designed structure should be open to the viewer, if we do not sacrifice function by so doing. Structure can be expressed by the shape of the product.

PERSONALITY

Each design should have its own personality. This is possible without sacrificing honesty, function, or structure. Personality is injected into a solution to a problem when the student is given the opportunity to design or modify a core problem. In this age of conformity—of living in similar homes, subdivisions, and with the mass production sentiment all about us—there are few opportunities for students to inject personality into their activities. Personality may be the most essential property of contemporary design.

if a problem is well designed, these factors are present

ITS FUNCTION IS APPARENT

A purposeful design is simple and to the point. Good design grows out of an analysis of the function of the product. The competent designer has a reason for every inch, curve or color that is included in the final problem.

THE TOOLS, EQUIPMENT AND PROCESSES USED FOR CONSTRUCTION OR FABRICATION ARE EVIDENT

Good workmanship is an inherent part of good design. Good craftsmanship endures only when it enhances good design. Good workmanship is an inherent part of good design.

THE MATERIAL OR MATERIALS CAN BE VISUALLY IDENTIFIED WITH NO DIFFICULTY

A purposeful design uses a minimum of materials.

IT REFLECTS A PERSONALITY OF "OUR AGE"

This is an "air age." The problem should also reflect the personality of the designer.

— CANDLE HOLDER —

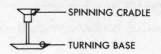

SPINNING CRADLE

TURNING BASE

SPINNING SCRATCHES
COPPER
COPPER PIPE
WALNUT
NATURAL FINISH
LINSEED OIL

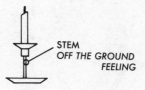

STEM
OFF THE GROUND FEELING

POOR ARRANGEMENT OF CRADLE AND BASE

•— design factors and the problem —•

the elements of design

The science of design has these basic symbols: line and shape, planes, solids and form, and surface quality which includes value, color and texture. All visual organization or design, regardless of how simple, complicated or spectacular, is the result of blending these visual ingredients.

LINES AND SHAPES ───────────────○

PLANES ───────────────────○

SOLIDS AND FORM ─────────────○

SURFACE VALUE, TEXTURE AND COLOR ──────○

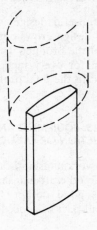

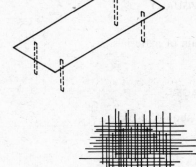

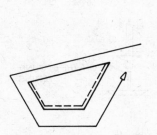

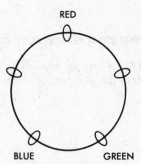

RED

BLUE   GREEN

lines and shapes

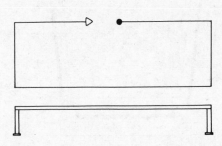

A line is the path of a point moving through space. It has only one dimension and DIRECTION is its most important property. Lines are the designer's connecting link between his mental image and the actual desired physical shape.

Lines help establish proportion and create the effect the designer has visualized. Properly conceived lines lead the wandering eye back and forth across the design, or shape, adding to the interest and retaining attention. Lines and combination of lines depict DIGNITY, REPOSE, ACTION and STABILITY.

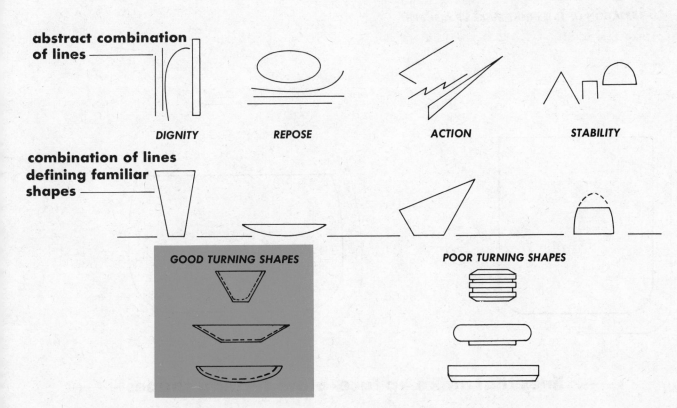

abstract combination of lines

DIGNITY   REPOSE   ACTION   STABILITY

combination of lines defining familiar shapes

GOOD TURNING SHAPES   POOR TURNING SHAPES

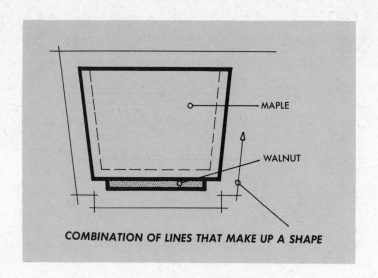

MAPLE

WALNUT

COMBINATION OF LINES THAT MAKE UP A SHAPE

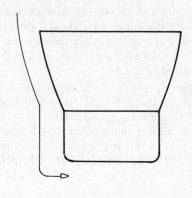

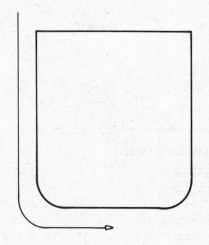

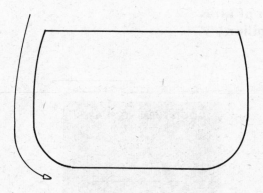

lines that make up face-plate turning shapes

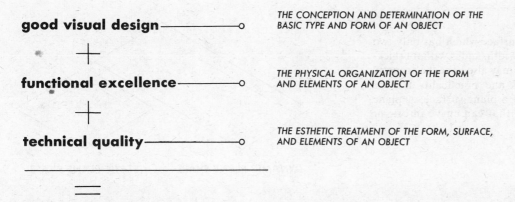

good visual design————o — THE CONCEPTION AND DETERMINATION OF THE BASIC TYPE AND FORM OF AN OBJECT

+

functional excellence————o — THE PHYSICAL ORGANIZATION OF THE FORM AND ELEMENTS OF AN OBJECT

+

technical quality————o — THE ESTHETIC TREATMENT OF THE FORM, SURFACE, AND ELEMENTS OF AN OBJECT

=

good end product

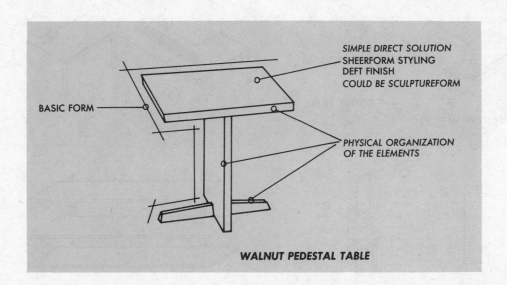

SIMPLE DIRECT SOLUTION
SHEERFORM STYLING
DEFT FINISH
COULD BE SCULPTUREFORM

BASIC FORM

PHYSICAL ORGANIZATION OF THE ELEMENTS

WALNUT PEDESTAL TABLE

o————— **good end product factors** ————o

planes

A plane is a flat, level surface which has only two dimensions, length and width, and is without thickness. A plane, like a line, may also have the property of direction. Usefulness and practicality are the principal advantages of a plane surface. A plane can be a flexible thing that can curve in one or more directions.

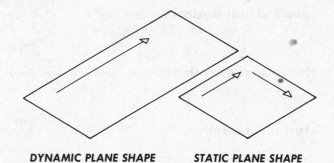

DYNAMIC PLANE SHAPE   **STATIC PLANE SHAPE**

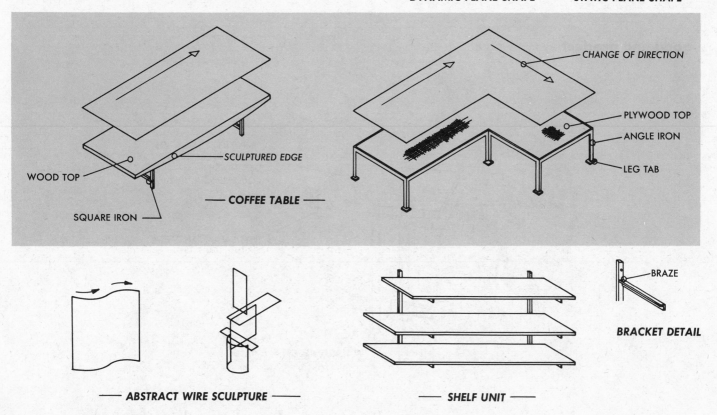

CHANGE OF DIRECTION

PLYWOOD TOP

ANGLE IRON

LEG TAB

SCULPTURED EDGE

WOOD TOP

— COFFEE TABLE —

SQUARE IRON

BRAZE

BRACKET DETAIL

— ABSTRACT WIRE SCULPTURE —   — SHELF UNIT —

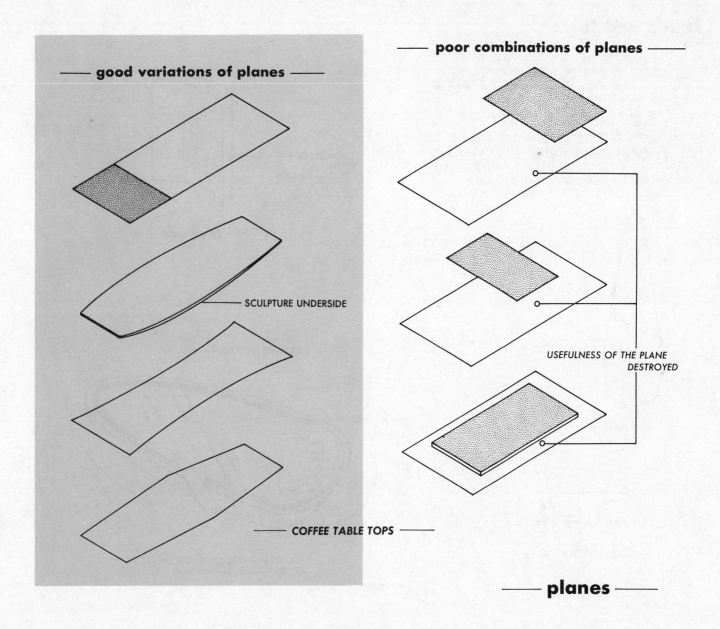

—— good variations of planes ——

SCULPTURE UNDERSIDE

USEFULNESS OF THE PLANE
DESTROYED

—— COFFEE TABLE TOPS ——

—— planes ——

17

solids and form

A solid is a three-dimensional object which occupies space. It may be open or closed and in addition to its exterior aspects, may also have an interior.

The important thing about any form is what is technically referred to as its "plastic quality," which is the pattern of contrasting light reflections which identify it. Sculptured surfaces usually predominate, and the result is pleasing to the eye.

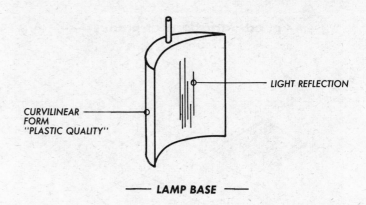

LIGHT REFLECTION

CURVILINEAR FORM "PLASTIC QUALITY"

— LAMP BASE —

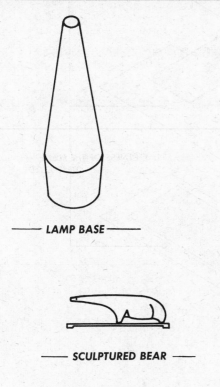

— LAMP BASE —

— SCULPTURED BEAR —

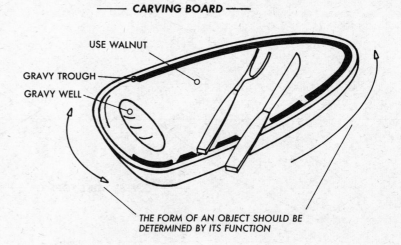

— CARVING BOARD —

USE WALNUT

GRAVY TROUGH

GRAVY WELL

THE FORM OF AN OBJECT SHOULD BE DETERMINED BY ITS FUNCTION

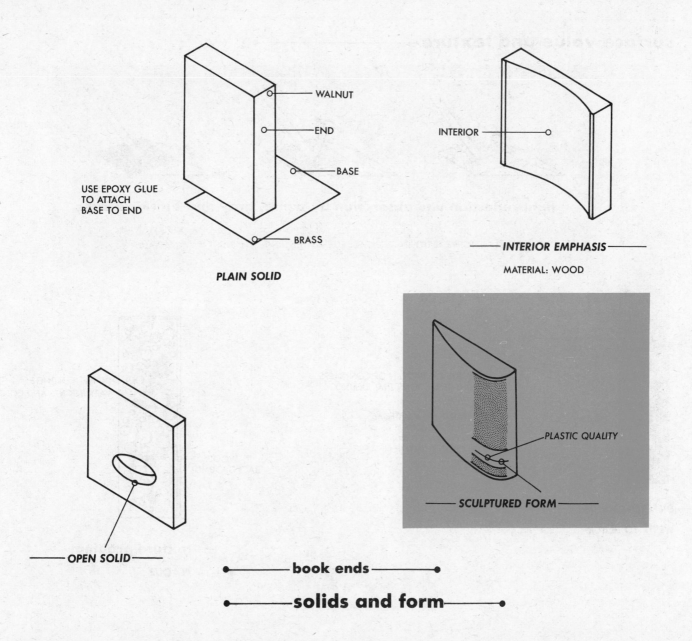

WALNUT

END

BASE

USE EPOXY GLUE
TO ATTACH
BASE TO END

BRASS

PLAIN SOLID

INTERIOR

——— *INTERIOR EMPHASIS* ———

MATERIAL: WOOD

PLASTIC QUALITY

SCULPTURED FORM

— OPEN SOLID —

●——— **book ends** ———●

●—— **solids and form** ——●

surface value and texture

light reflection and absorption by white, gray and black surfaces

THE OVER-ALL REFLECTIVE ABILITY OF A SURFACE FOR ALL THE LIGHT STRIKING IT IS CALLED VALUE.

TEXTURE IS THE PATTERN OF CONTRASTS IN LIGHT REFLECTIONS THAT IDENTIFY THE SURFACE.

THE BEAUTY OF A MATERIAL AND OF A PROBLEM IS OFTEN ENHANCED BY EMPHASIZING TEXTURE.

DOWEL CUTTINGS
VARY HEIGHTS AND COLOR

WOOD
BACKGROUND

— DIFFERENT VALUES —

WHITE TO BLACK

— texture problem —

● — PLAQUE

surface color ————————○

The color wheel shown is based on the Munsell Color System. It has FIVE PRIMARY COLORS:
RED
YELLOW
GREEN
BLUE
PURPLE.

Pairs of ADJACENT COLORS on the wheel are known as HARMONIOUS HUES. Colors OPPOSITE to each other are COMPLEMENTARIES.

The skill of controlling surface color has been carefully studied by the Industrial Designer as a means of increasing contrast and adding interest to a design. The designer ranks color as a design element second only to line and form.

Color if properly used can have great aesthetic appeal. Color has a definite effect on other design elements.

RED

RED-PURPLE   RED-YELLOW

PURPLE

← COLOR WHEEL →   YELLOW

BLUE-PURPLE   YELLOW-GREEN

COMPLEMENTARY COLORS PAIR

Film Bibliography;
DISCOVERING COLOR
17 minutes
Differences in color as to hue, value and intensity. Blending of paints in terms of these variations. Variety applications of color principles.
(University of Michigan Film Library)

BLUE   GREEN

BLUE-GREEN

HARMONIOUS HUES FAMILY OF GREEN

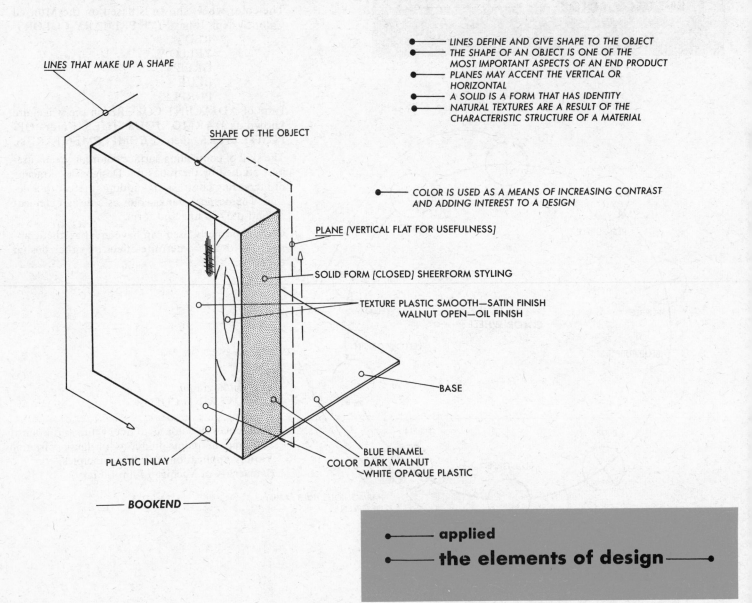

LINES THAT MAKE UP A SHAPE

SHAPE OF THE OBJECT

LINES DEFINE AND GIVE SHAPE TO THE OBJECT
THE SHAPE OF AN OBJECT IS ONE OF THE
MOST IMPORTANT ASPECTS OF AN END PRODUCT
PLANES MAY ACCENT THE VERTICAL OR
HORIZONTAL
A SOLID IS A FORM THAT HAS IDENTITY
NATURAL TEXTURES ARE A RESULT OF THE
CHARACTERISTIC STRUCTURE OF A MATERIAL

COLOR IS USED AS A MEANS OF INCREASING CONTRAST
AND ADDING INTEREST TO A DESIGN

PLANE [VERTICAL FLAT FOR USEFULNESS]

SOLID FORM [CLOSED] SHEERFORM STYLING

TEXTURE PLASTIC SMOOTH—SATIN FINISH
WALNUT OPEN—OIL FINISH

BASE

BLUE ENAMEL
COLOR DARK WALNUT
WHITE OPAQUE PLASTIC

PLASTIC INLAY

BOOKEND

applied
the elements of design

22

the principles of design ————————————————————————

In general there are characteristics common to
most good designs. Among these are unity, variety,
balance, proportion, and rhythm, the principles by
which the four elements of design are bound
together.

UNITY AND VARIETY ————————————————————————o

BALANCE AND SYMMETRY ————————————————————o

PROPORTION ————————————————————————————o

RHYTHM ————————————————————————————————o

unity and variety

harmony

Unity and variety are the means by which we analyze the overall effect of design. If a design has unity we mean that everything in it is woven together, according to some well laid plan. Another name for unity is harmony. Harmony is when all the elements in the design get along well together. When there is harmony, there is the oneness of unity, and a pleasing overall effect.

Variety means the use of contrasting elements so controlled and placed as to hold and retain our attention. When one's eye can move smoothly around the design instead of having to jump from one element to another, there is unity. Variety is introduced to prevent excessive repetition and the monotony it produces.

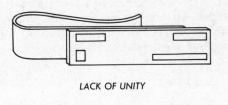

LACK OF UNITY

ARRANGEMENT OF SHAPES

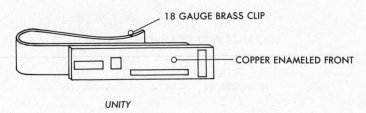

18 GAUGE BRASS CLIP

COPPER ENAMELED FRONT

UNITY

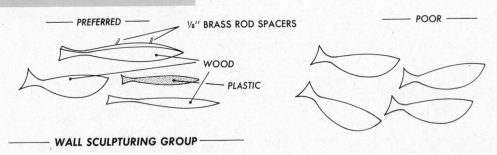

PREFERRED — ⅛" BRASS ROD SPACERS

WOOD

PLASTIC

POOR

WALL SCULPTURING GROUP

VARIETY—SHAPES AND MATERIALS

LACKS VARIETY OF SHAPES

IN THIS PROBLEM NOTE:

Variety of sizes of enamel shapes
Variety of color of enamel shapes
Variety of spaced enamel shapes
Variety of heights of enamel shapes
Variety of texture of walnut back and glazed enamel shapes

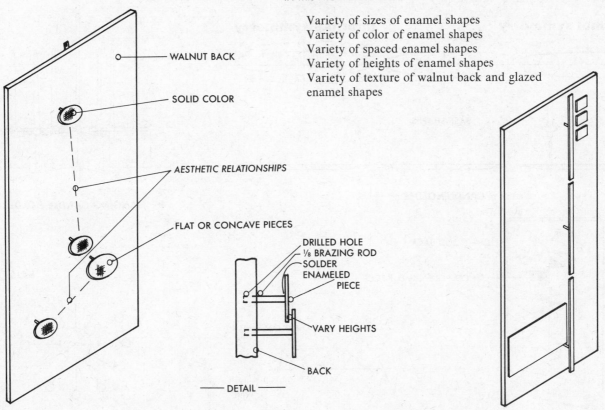

WALNUT BACK

SOLID COLOR

AESTHETIC RELATIONSHIPS

FLAT OR CONCAVE PIECES

DRILLED HOLE
⅛ BRAZING ROD
SOLDER
ENAMELED
PIECE

VARY HEIGHTS

BACK

— DETAIL —

●——**3-dimensional enamel plaques**
●——**unity and variety**——●

25

balance and symmetry

Balance we can see is known as optical balance. When the two halves of an object are exactly alike on either side of an axis the relation is known as formal symmetry. Balance need not be a strictly formal arrangement.

formal symmetry   ## informal symmetry

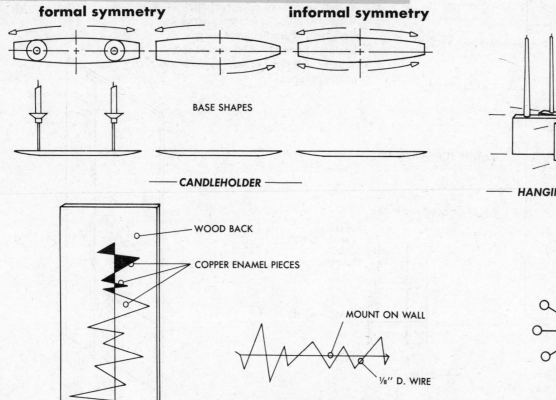

BASE SHAPES

— CANDLEHOLDER —

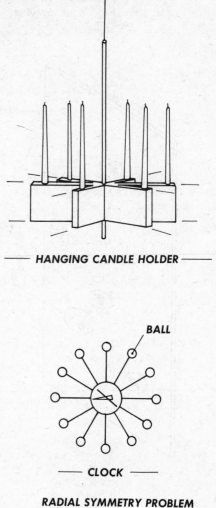

— HANGING CANDLE HOLDER —

WOOD BACK

COPPER ENAMEL PIECES

MOUNT ON WALL

⅛″ D. WIRE

— WIRE SCULPTURE —

INFORMAL SYMMETRY PROBLEM

— PLAQUE —

BALL

— CLOCK —

RADIAL SYMMETRY PROBLEM

FOR CLOCK MOVEMENTS

School Products Co., 312 East 23rd Street, New York 10, N. Y.

POSSIBLE MATERIALS:
WOOD
METAL
GLASS
PLEXIGLAS
MOSAIC TILE

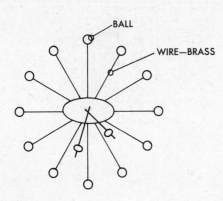

BALL

WIRE—BRASS

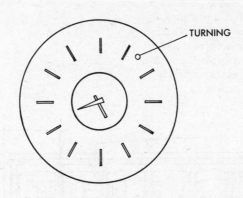

TURNING

BOND WOOD TO METAL WITH EPOXY GLUE

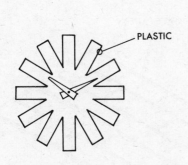

PLASTIC

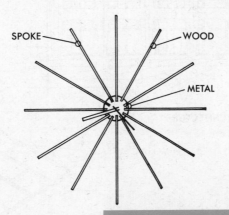

SPOKE

WOOD

METAL

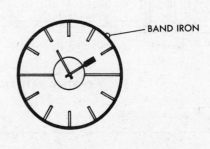

BAND IRON

CLOCKS

radial symmetry problems

27

rhythm

The feeling of rhythm in a design is obtained by the repetition of forms, lines, curves, colors, textures, etc. Rhythm produces a feeling of pleasing motion as the eye looks over the object. Rhythm in design is marked by a regular occurrence of, or alternation in, features or elements. It is the nature of rhythm to be recurring in a regular manner so that you can depend on it, you expect it.

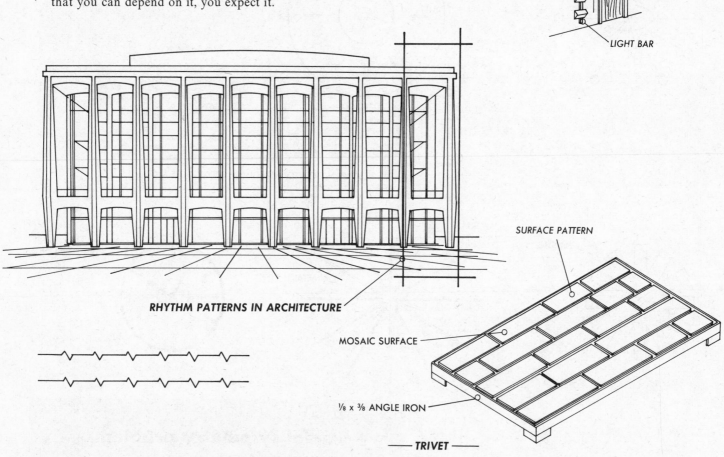

RHYTHM PATTERN

LIGHT BAR

RHYTHM PATTERNS IN ARCHITECTURE

SURFACE PATTERN

MOSAIC SURFACE

⅛ x ⅜ ANGLE IRON

—— TRIVET ——

proportion ●————————————————●

Proportion means the size relation of one portion to another or of part to the whole. Proportion is one of the most effective means of creating unity among the various components.

When proportion is well handled, a problem has a feeling of gracefulness.

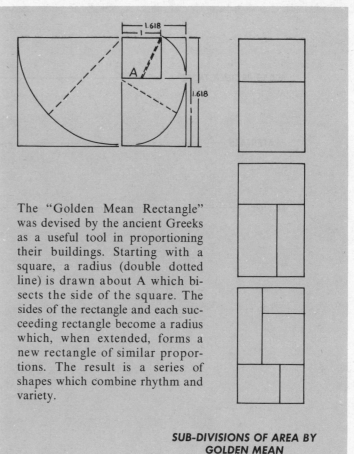

The "Golden Mean Rectangle" was devised by the ancient Greeks as a useful tool in proportioning their buildings. Starting with a square, a radius (double dotted line) is drawn about A which bisects the side of the square. The sides of the rectangle and each succeeding rectangle become a radius which, when extended, forms a new rectangle of similar proportions. The result is a series of shapes which combine rhythm and variety.

SUB-DIVISIONS OF AREA BY GOLDEN MEAN

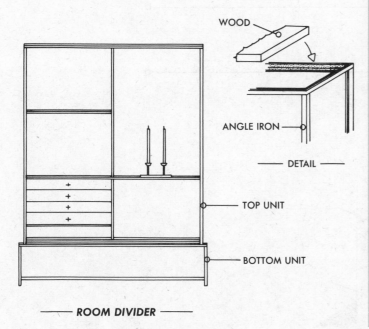

WOOD

ANGLE IRON

——— DETAIL

——— TOP UNIT

——— BOTTOM UNIT

——— ROOM DIVIDER ———

understanding today's products with relation to:

MASS PRODUCTION ⎯⎯⎯⎯⎯⎯⎯⎯⎯⎯⎯⎯⎯⎯○

MATERIALS ⎯⎯⎯⎯⎯⎯⎯⎯⎯⎯⎯⎯⎯⎯⎯○

DESIGN ⎯⎯⎯⎯⎯⎯⎯⎯⎯⎯⎯⎯⎯⎯⎯○

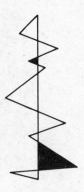

design and technical terms ————————————

DESIGN ————————————————————————————— *A SIMPLE AND DIRECT SOLUTION TO A PROBLEM*

CREATIVITY ————————————————————————— *IMPROVING OLD IDEAS*
COMBINING OLD IDEAS CONSTRUCTIVELY
CREATING NEW IDEAS

PRACTICAL DESIGN ———————————————————— *A DESIGN APPROACH USED IN ENGINEERING, ARCHITECTURE, INDUSTRIAL DESIGN AND INDUSTRIAL ARTS*

MACHINE AGE ————————————————————————— *TODAY'S TECHNICAL KNOW-HOW PLUS THE NEEDS OF MODERN MAN*

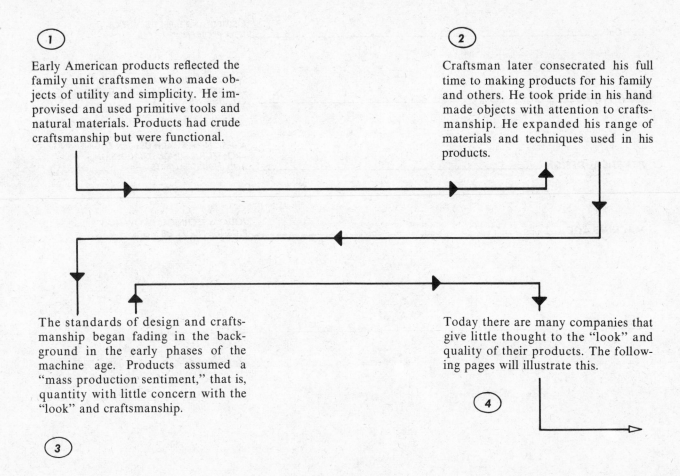

1

Early American products reflected the family unit craftsmen who made objects of utility and simplicity. He improvised and used primitive tools and natural materials. Products had crude craftsmanship but were functional.

2

Craftsman later consecrated his full time to making products for his family and others. He took pride in his hand made objects with attention to craftsmanship. He expanded his range of materials and techniques used in his products.

3

The standards of design and craftsmanship began fading in the background in the early phases of the machine age. Products assumed a "mass production sentiment," that is, quantity with little concern with the "look" and craftsmanship.

4

Today there are many companies that give little thought to the "look" and quality of their products. The following pages will illustrate this.

mass production sentiment designs——3

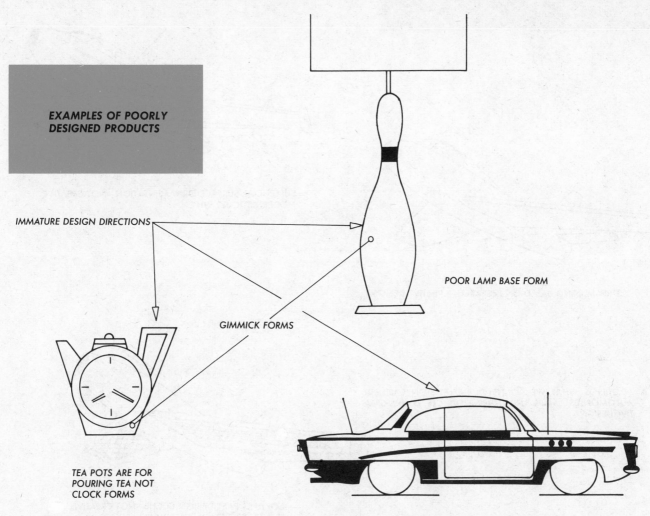

EXAMPLES OF POORLY
DESIGNED PRODUCTS

IMMATURE DESIGN DIRECTIONS

GIMMICK FORMS

POOR LAMP BASE FORM

TEA POTS ARE FOR
POURING TEA NOT
CLOCK FORMS

SUPERFICIAL SURFACE ORNAMENTATION

mass-production sentiment designs

distortion of values——4

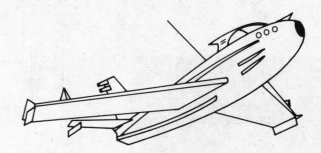

SUPERFICIAL SURFACE ORNAMENTATION—NOT CREATIVE
MODERNISTIC JET WHY?

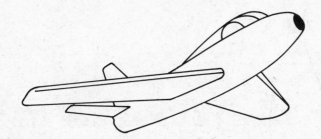

STREAMLINING BASED ON RESEARCH—CREATIVE DESIGN

THIS IS WHAT WE DO TO OUR TELEVISION CABINETS,
AUTOMOBILES, LAMPS AND OTHER PRODUCTS. IS THIS CREA-
TIVE DESIGN?

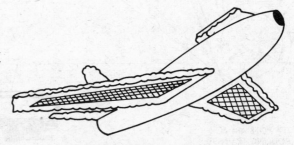

COPYING PAST DESIGN CLICHE—NOT CREATIVE
FRENCH PROVINCIAL JET—WHY?

The streamlining of an airplane is based upon research. The airplane represents one of the most creative endeavors of our technical society.

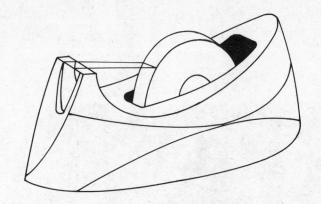

IT LOOKS AS IF IT IS ABOUT TO TAKE OFF

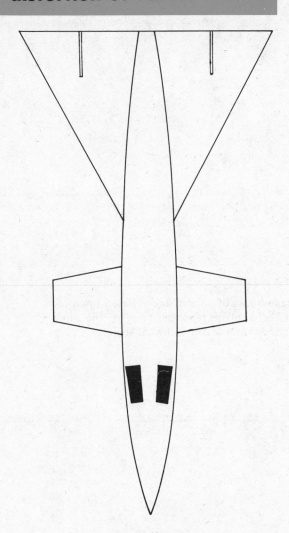

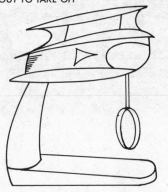

TOO STREAMLINED FOR A KITCHEN ATMOSPHERE

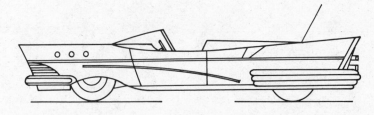

SUPERFICIAL SURFACE ORNAMENTATION

(1) STREAMLINING BASED ON RESEARCH

(2) FICTITIOUS STREAMLINING

the industrial designing process——6

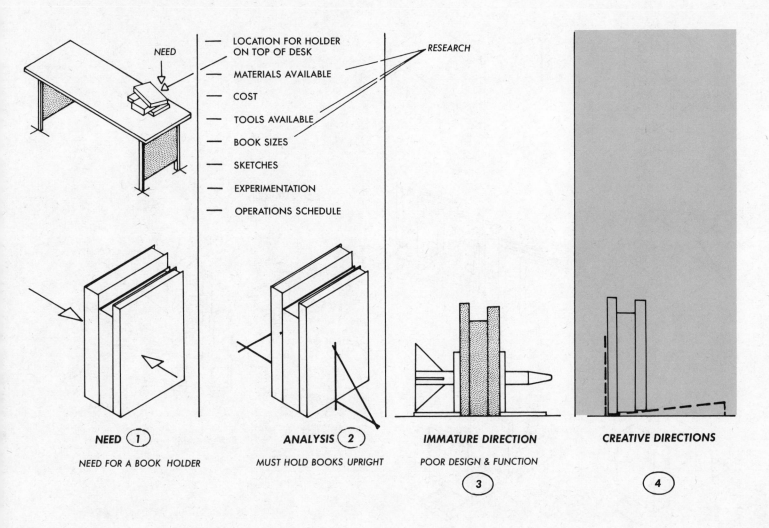

NEED

- LOCATION FOR HOLDER ON TOP OF DESK
- MATERIALS AVAILABLE
- COST
- TOOLS AVAILABLE
- BOOK SIZES
- SKETCHES
- EXPERIMENTATION
- OPERATIONS SCHEDULE

RESEARCH

NEED ①

NEED FOR A BOOK HOLDER

ANALYSIS ②

MUST HOLD BOOKS UPRIGHT

IMMATURE DIRECTION

POOR DESIGN & FUNCTION

③

CREATIVE DIRECTIONS

④

creative solutions——7

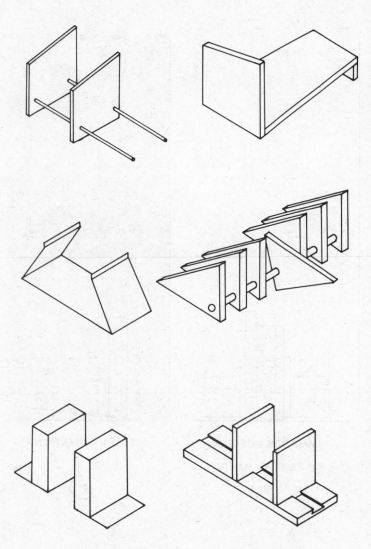

a simple and direct solution to a problem——8

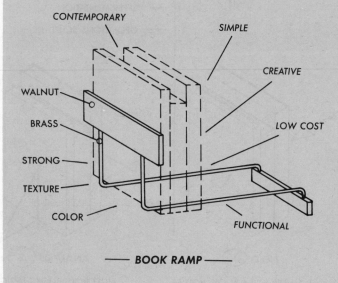

CONTEMPORARY

SIMPLE

CREATIVE

WALNUT

BRASS

STRONG

TEXTURE

COLOR

LOW COST

FUNCTIONAL

——— BOOK RAMP ———

Book Ramp
    Note: Sculptured wood members

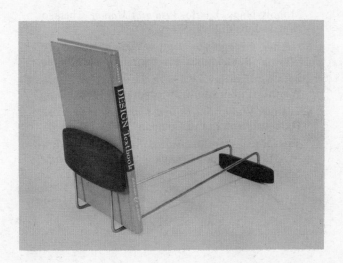

basic contemporary design references

BOOKS AND BOOKLETS

Kaufmann, Edgar, Jr., *What is Modern Design?* New York: The Museum of Modern Art, 1950, 32 pp.

*Lindbeck, John R., *Design Textbook.* Bloomington, Illinois: McKnight & McKnight Publishing Company, 1963, 163 pp.

Moholy-Nagy, Laszlo, *Vision in Motion,* Chicago: Paul Theobald, 1947, 371 pp.

Nelson, George, *Problems of Design,* New York: Whitney Publications, Incorporated, 1961, 206 pp.

Sutnar, Ladislav, *Package Design,* New York: Whitney Publications, Incorporated, 1962, 190 pp.

Teaque, Walter D., *Design This Day.* New York: Harcourt, Brace, and Company, 1940, 291 pp.

Van Doren, Harold, *Industrial Design.* New York: McGraw-Hill Book Company, Incorporated, 1954, 379 pp.

PERIODICALS

Craft Horizons, 29 West 43rd Street, New York 13, New York.

Design, 337 South High Street, Columbus, Ohio.

Design Quarterly, 1710 South Lyndale Avenue, Minneapolis 5, Minnesota.

* *Industrial Design,* 18 East 50th Street, New York 22, New York.

FILMS

*"American Look." Jam Handy Organization, 2821 East Grand Boulevard, Detroit 11, Michigan.

Core reference materials for introducing design in industrial arts activities.

So that students and faculty may see and in turn appreciate the design efforts of the individual pupils of the industrial arts classes, a continuous school display is suggested. The display, either a lobby or window display, should be a part of an overall industrial arts program. We must continually present to others examples of good design so they in turn will acquire an appreciation for contemporary solutions to problems. The reactions and suggestions of others as they view the different problems may improve our efforts toward better designed items. The photographs presented here are typical of a free-standing school lobby display used successfully in our school.

2—Dimensional Graphics

Note: Contact paper cutout letters (vary the colors) vertical display panel
2- and 3-dimensional information and problems displayed side by side
Sculpturing, lamination, and graphics problems

Typical Free-Standing School Lobby Display
Note: Vertical and horizontal accent
      Total concept of industrial arts activities

Mahogany Tri-Paneled Stand-Up Display
Note: Horizontal stringer-supported shelf
    display
    Spinning, enameling and raising problems

Patio Display Table

    Note: Gravel texture of surface table
           How the table surface is divided up
           Sculpturing, lamination, plastic, mosaic,
             turning and brazing problems

Stand-Up Pegboard Display Panel

    Note: Spotlight above panel on overhead beam
           Shelf and stringer construction
           Turning, screening, leather, sheet metal
             and electronics problems

Back Side of Stand-Up Pegboard Display Panel
Note: Sheet metal surface development problems

Back Side of Tri-panel
Note: Burlap and cork textured strips
Mosaic problems

44

CHAPTER **2**

WOOD SCULPTURING

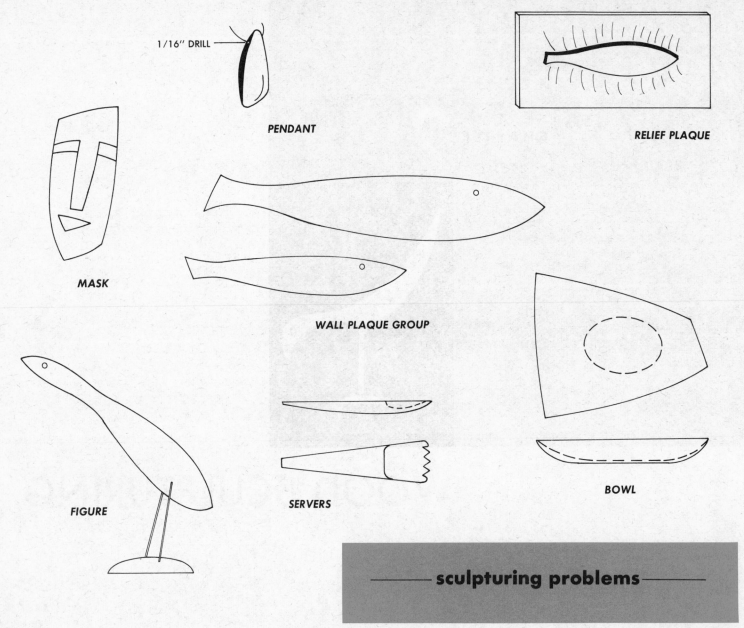

1/16" DRILL

PENDANT

RELIEF PLAQUE

MASK

WALL PLAQUE GROUP

FIGURE

SERVERS

BOWL

sculpturing problems

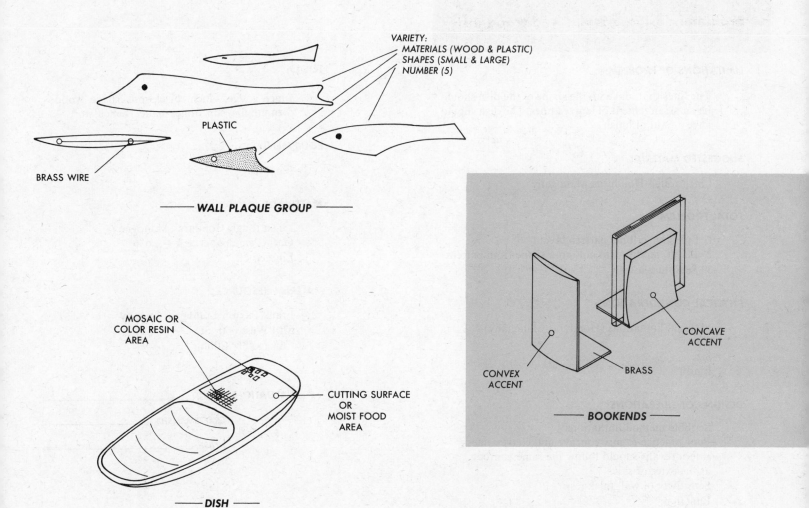

VARIETY:
MATERIALS (WOOD & PLASTIC)
SHAPES (SMALL & LARGE)
NUMBER (5)

PLASTIC

BRASS WIRE

WALL PLAQUE GROUP

MOSAIC OR
COLOR RESIN
AREA

CUTTING SURFACE
OR
MOIST FOOD
AREA

DISH

CONVEX
ACCENT

BRASS

CONCAVE
ACCENT

BOOKENDS

sculpturing ideas

47

core problem: dish

problem: design a sculptured wood dish

LIMITATIONS OF PROBLEM:

The lines that make up the shape of the dish should be an arrangement of convex lines. The dish should have a natural finish.

SUGGESTED MATERIAL:

1 inch rough Honduras Mahogany

TOTAL PROBLEM:

1. Full size scribble pattern layout
2. Select, modify and cut out a shape from pattern
3. Sculpture a dish

PHYSICAL CONSIDERATIONS:

Material limitations (Honduras Mahogany)
Cost
Size
Finish

DESIGN CONSIDERATIONS:

Scribble method limitations
Poor practice to mix concave and convex lines
Interior walls should follow the same contour
as the exterior sides
Sensitivity of wall thickness
Function
Shape
Finish (linseed oil)
Surface treatment (smooth or gouge marks)

TOOLS:

1 inch gouge, 1 inch chisel, spokeshave, wood forming file, slip stone, mallet, bench stop

EQUIPMENT:

Bandsaw

MATERIALS:

1 inch rough Honduras Mahogany
Garnet sandpaper #2—#o/6
Linseed oil

MATERIAL RESOURCE:

Frank Paxton Lumber Company
5701 West 66th St.
Chicago 38, Illinois

EVALUATION: DESIGN _____

CRAFTSMANSHIP _____

FINISH _____

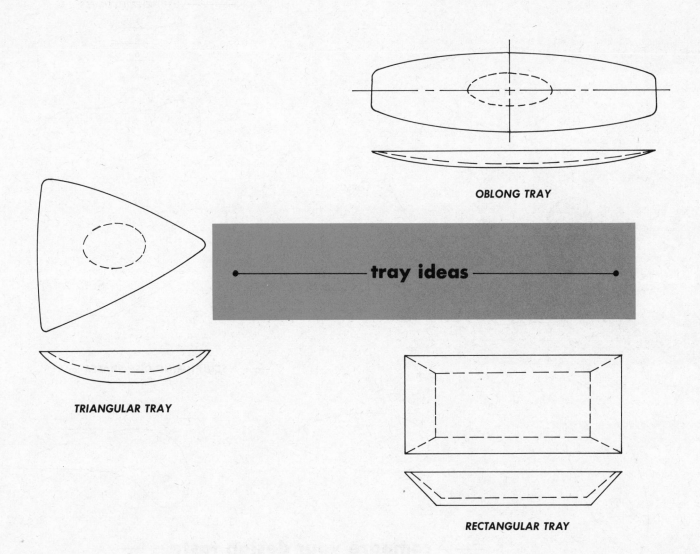

OBLONG TRAY

tray ideas

TRIANGULAR TRAY

RECTANGULAR TRAY

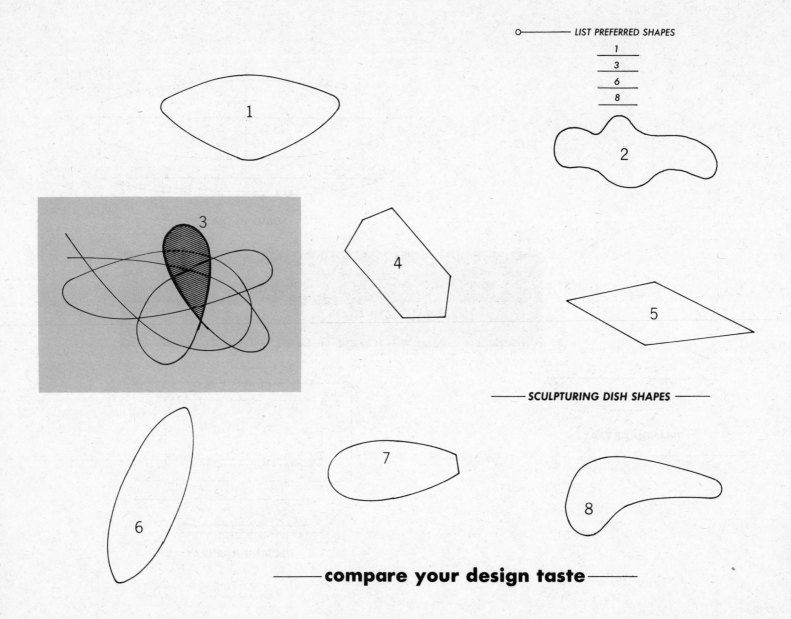

LIST PREFERRED SHAPES

1
3
6
8

SCULPTURING DISH SHAPES

compare your design taste

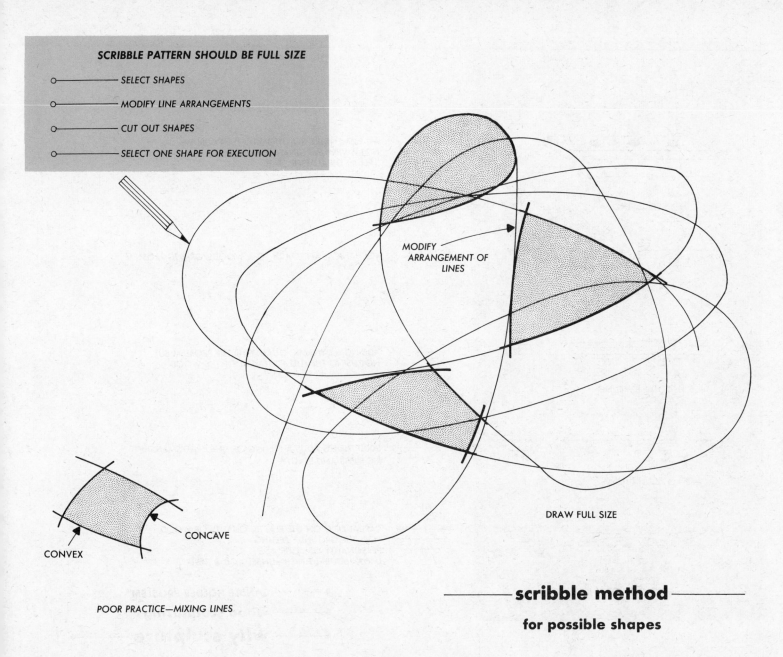

MODIFY
ARRANGEMENT OF
LINES

DRAW FULL SIZE

CONCAVE

CONVEX

POOR PRACTICE—MIXING LINES

scribble method

for possible shapes

51

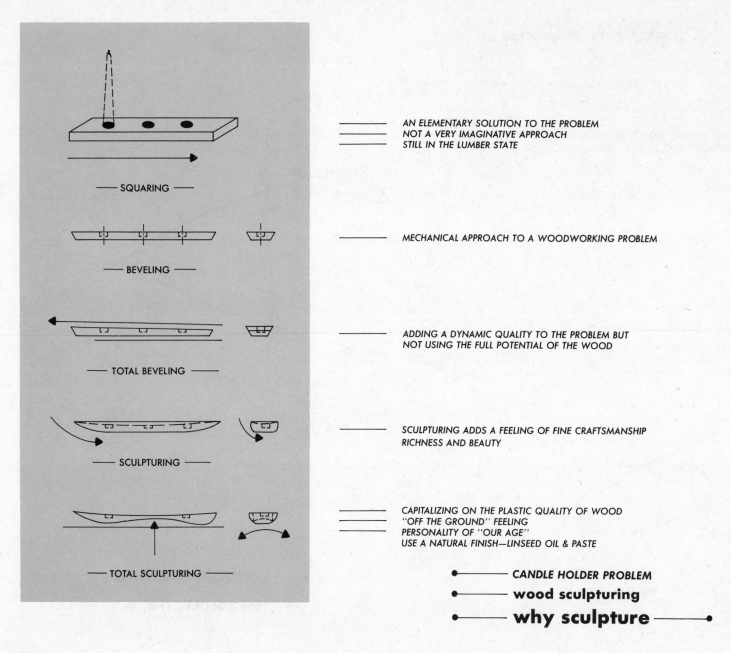

SQUARING

AN ELEMENTARY SOLUTION TO THE PROBLEM
NOT A VERY IMAGINATIVE APPROACH
STILL IN THE LUMBER STATE

BEVELING

MECHANICAL APPROACH TO A WOODWORKING PROBLEM

TOTAL BEVELING

ADDING A DYNAMIC QUALITY TO THE PROBLEM BUT
NOT USING THE FULL POTENTIAL OF THE WOOD

SCULPTURING

SCULPTURING ADDS A FEELING OF FINE CRAFTSMANSHIP
RICHNESS AND BEAUTY

TOTAL SCULPTURING

CAPITALIZING ON THE PLASTIC QUALITY OF WOOD
"OFF THE GROUND" FEELING
PERSONALITY OF "OUR AGE"
USE A NATURAL FINISH—LINSEED OIL & PASTE

CANDLE HOLDER PROBLEM

wood sculpturing

why sculpture

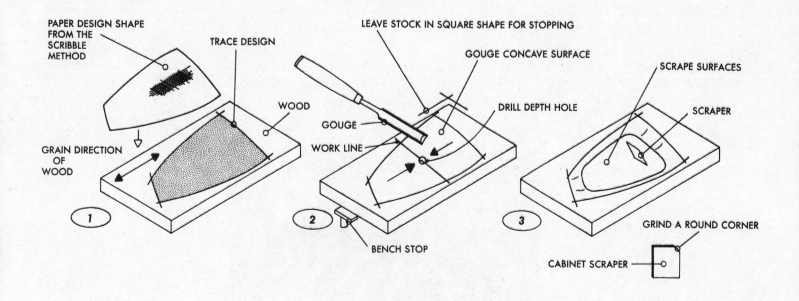

1. PAPER DESIGN SHAPE FROM THE SCRIBBLE METHOD — TRACE DESIGN — WOOD — GRAIN DIRECTION OF WOOD

2. LEAVE STOCK IN SQUARE SHAPE FOR STOPPING — GOUGE CONCAVE SURFACE — DRILL DEPTH HOLE — GOUGE — WORK LINE — BENCH STOP

3. SCRAPE SURFACES — SCRAPER — GRIND A ROUND CORNER — CABINET SCRAPER

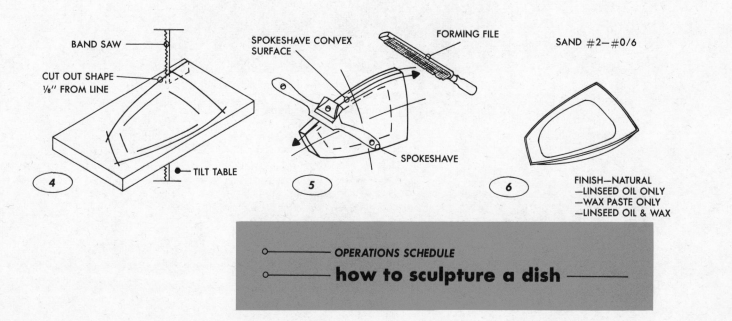

4. BAND SAW — CUT OUT SHAPE 1/8" FROM LINE — TILT TABLE

5. SPOKESHAVE CONVEX SURFACE — FORMING FILE — SPOKESHAVE

6. SAND #2—#0/6 — FINISH—NATURAL —LINSEED OIL ONLY —WAX PASTE ONLY —LINSEED OIL & WAX

OPERATIONS SCHEDULE

how to sculpture a dish

Wood Tray
Note: Triangular shape
Concave surface

By introducing ceramic tile into this problem you bring in play:

TEXTURE (ceramic tile, high gloss surface— wood, rich deep surface)

COLOR (ceramic tile color—wood color)

UTILITY (cutting area or moist food area)

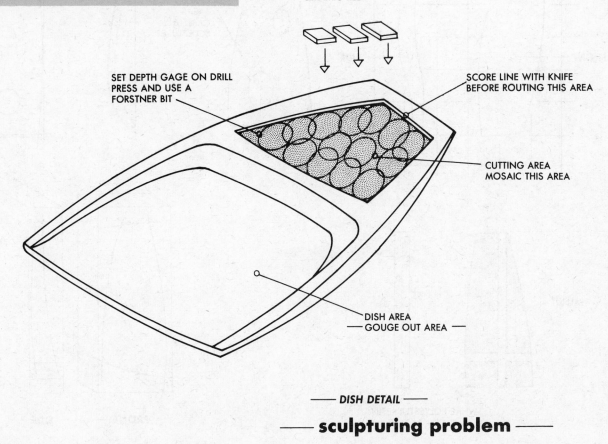

CERAMIC TILE

SET DEPTH GAGE ON DRILL PRESS AND USE A FORSTNER BIT

SCORE LINE WITH KNIFE BEFORE ROUTING THIS AREA

CUTTING AREA MOSAIC THIS AREA

DISH AREA — GOUGE OUT AREA —

— DISH DETAIL —

— **sculpturing problem** —

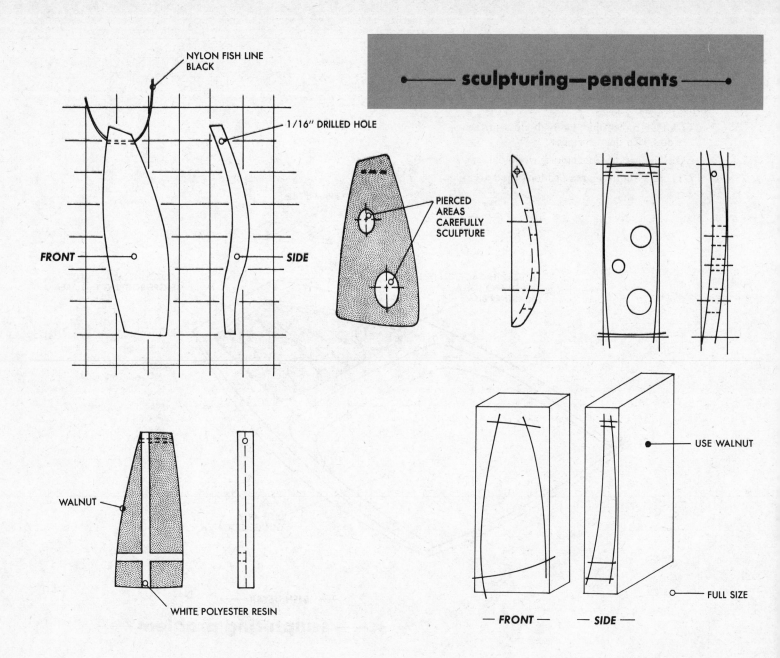

NYLON FISH LINE
BLACK

1/16" DRILLED HOLE

FRONT

SIDE

PIERCED
AREAS
CAREFULLY
SCULPTURE

WALNUT

WHITE POLYESTER RESIN

USE WALNUT

FULL SIZE

— FRONT —   — SIDE —

56

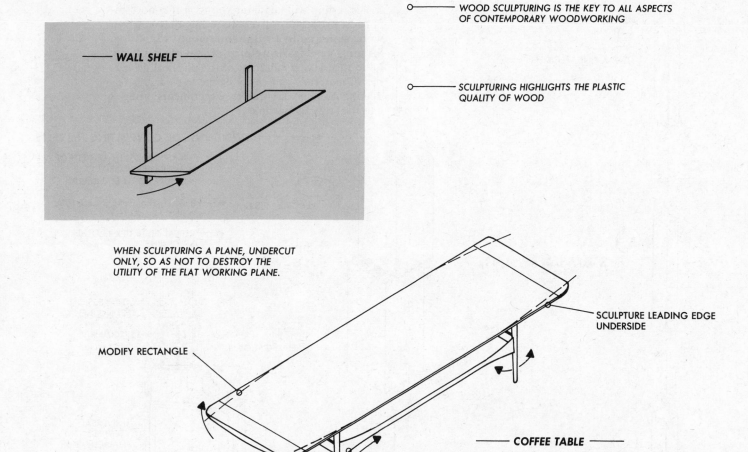

WALL SHELF

WOOD SCULPTURING IS THE KEY TO ALL ASPECTS
OF CONTEMPORARY WOODWORKING

SCULPTURING HIGHLIGHTS THE PLASTIC
QUALITY OF WOOD

WHEN SCULPTURING A PLANE, UNDERCUT
ONLY, SO AS NOT TO DESTROY THE
UTILITY OF THE FLAT WORKING PLANE.

SCULPTURE LEADING EDGE
UNDERSIDE

MODIFY RECTANGLE

COFFEE TABLE

SCULPTURE

wood sculpturing

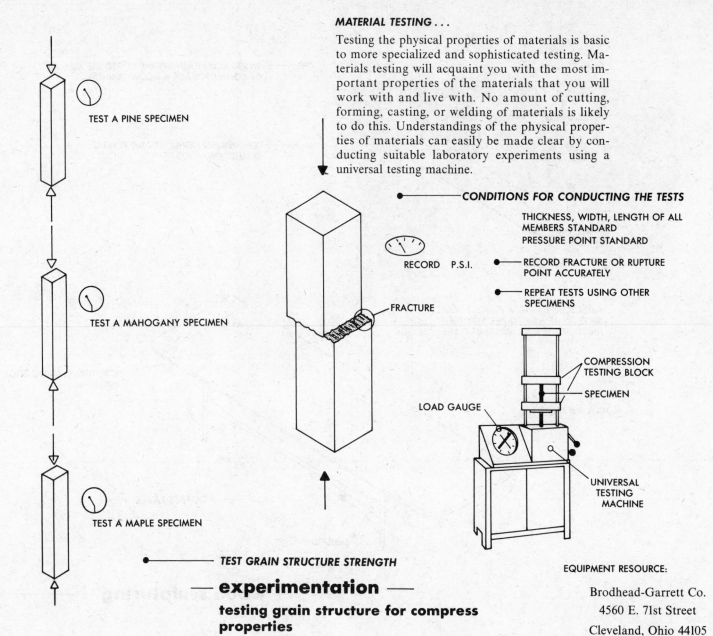

TEST A PINE SPECIMEN

TEST A MAHOGANY SPECIMEN

TEST A MAPLE SPECIMEN

MATERIAL TESTING...

Testing the physical properties of materials is basic to more specialized and sophisticated testing. Materials testing will acquaint you with the most important properties of the materials that you will work with and live with. No amount of cutting, forming, casting, or welding of materials is likely to do this. Understandings of the physical properties of materials can easily be made clear by conducting suitable laboratory experiments using a universal testing machine.

RECORD P.S.I.

FRACTURE

CONDITIONS FOR CONDUCTING THE TESTS

THICKNESS, WIDTH, LENGTH OF ALL MEMBERS STANDARD
PRESSURE POINT STANDARD

RECORD FRACTURE OR RUPTURE POINT ACCURATELY

REPEAT TESTS USING OTHER SPECIMENS

COMPRESSION TESTING BLOCK

SPECIMEN

LOAD GAUGE

UNIVERSAL TESTING MACHINE

TEST GRAIN STRUCTURE STRENGTH

experimentation —
testing grain structure for compress properties

EQUIPMENT RESOURCE:

Brodhead-Garrett Co.
4560 E. 71st Street
Cleveland, Ohio 44105

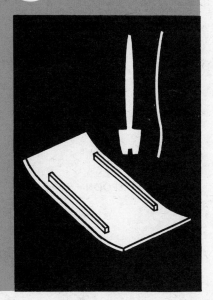

CHAPTER 3

WOOD LAMINATION

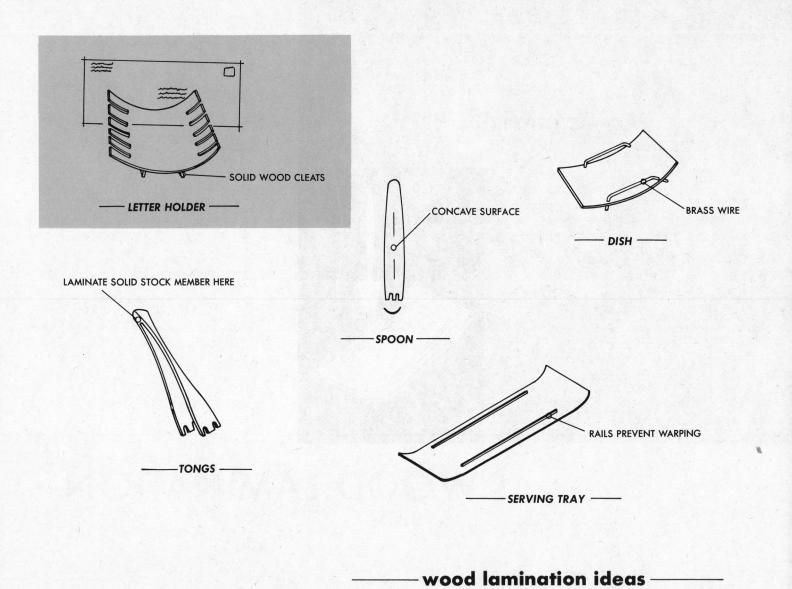

SOLID WOOD CLEATS

LETTER HOLDER

LAMINATE SOLID STOCK MEMBER HERE

TONGS

CONCAVE SURFACE

SPOON

BRASS WIRE

DISH

RAILS PREVENT WARPING

SERVING TRAY

wood lamination ideas

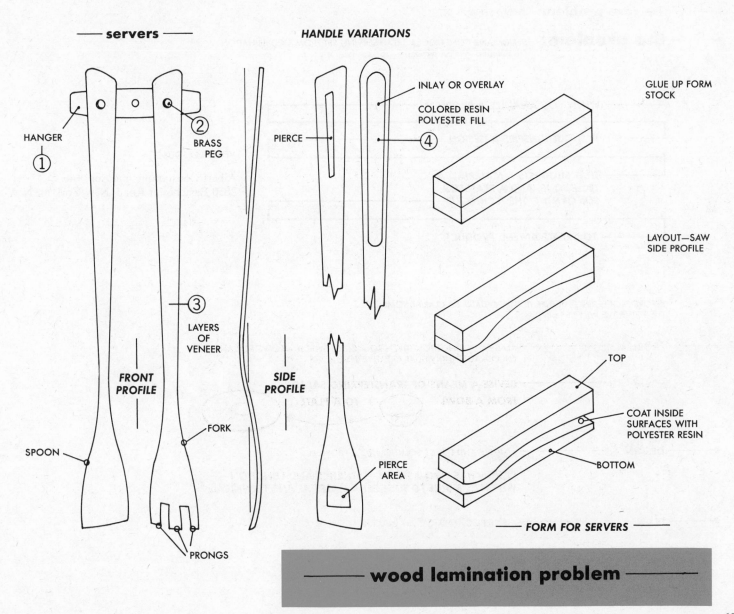

servers ——

HANDLE VARIATIONS

HANGER
①

BRASS
PEG
②

INLAY OR OVERLAY

COLORED RESIN
POLYESTER FILL

PIERCE

④

③

LAYERS
OF
VENEER

FRONT
PROFILE

SIDE
PROFILE

FORK

SPOON

PIERCE
AREA

PRONGS

GLUE UP FORM
STOCK

LAYOUT—SAW
SIDE PROFILE

TOP

COAT INSIDE
SURFACES WITH
POLYESTER RESIN

BOTTOM

—— FORM FOR SERVERS ——

—— wood lamination problem ——

the core problem: *SALAD SERVING SET*

the problem: *DESIGN AND CONSTRUCT A SALAD SERVING SET FROM A COMBINATION OF BONDED VENEER LAYERS*

WHEN YOU ANALYZE A PROBLEM

IT SHOULD INSPIRE A DESIGN

THAT SUGGESTS A MATERIAL, A TECHNIQUE, AND A PLAN FOR PERFORMING THE TECHNIQUE

TO CREATE AN END PRODUCT

VENEER RESOURCE:

Albert Constantine and Son, Inc.
2050 Eastchester Road, New York 61, N. Y.

BEFORE PROCEEDING FURTHER IT IS IMPORTANT TO CLARIFY SOME OF THE TERMS WE WILL BE USING:

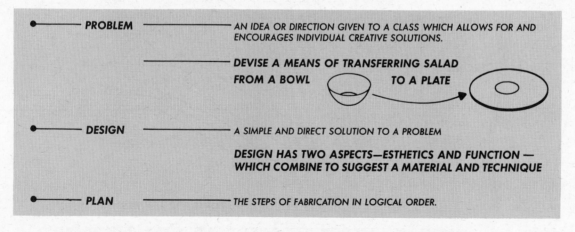

PROBLEM — *AN IDEA OR DIRECTION GIVEN TO A CLASS WHICH ALLOWS FOR AND ENCOURAGES INDIVIDUAL CREATIVE SOLUTIONS.*

DEVISE A MEANS OF TRANSFERRING SALAD FROM A BOWL **TO A PLATE**

DESIGN — *A SIMPLE AND DIRECT SOLUTION TO A PROBLEM*

DESIGN HAS TWO ASPECTS—ESTHETICS AND FUNCTION — WHICH COMBINE TO SUGGEST A MATERIAL AND TECHNIQUE

PLAN — *THE STEPS OF FABRICATION IN LOGICAL ORDER.*

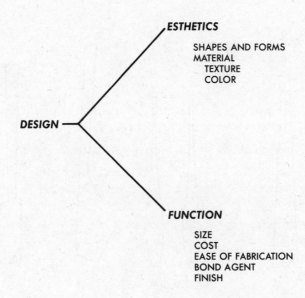

ESTHETICS

SHAPES AND FORMS
MATERIAL
TEXTURE
COLOR

DESIGN

FUNCTION

SIZE
COST
EASE OF FABRICATION
BOND AGENT
FINISH

design considerations

63

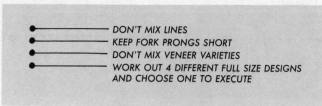

- DON'T MIX LINES
- KEEP FORK PRONGS SHORT
- DON'T MIX VENEER VARIETIES
- WORK OUT 4 DIFFERENT FULL SIZE DESIGNS AND CHOOSE ONE TO EXECUTE

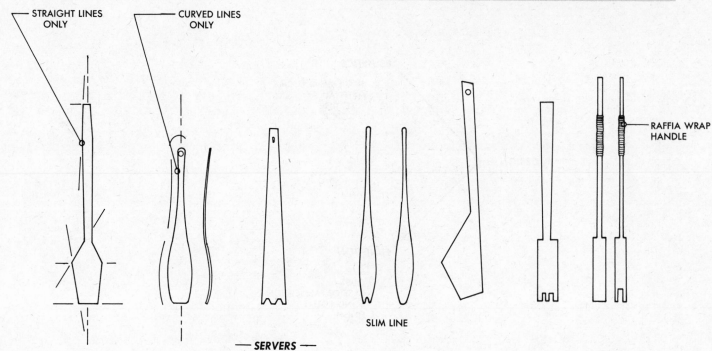

STRAIGHT LINES ONLY

CURVED LINES ONLY

RAFFIA WRAP HANDLE

SLIM LINE

— SERVERS —

— **wood lamination design possibilities** —

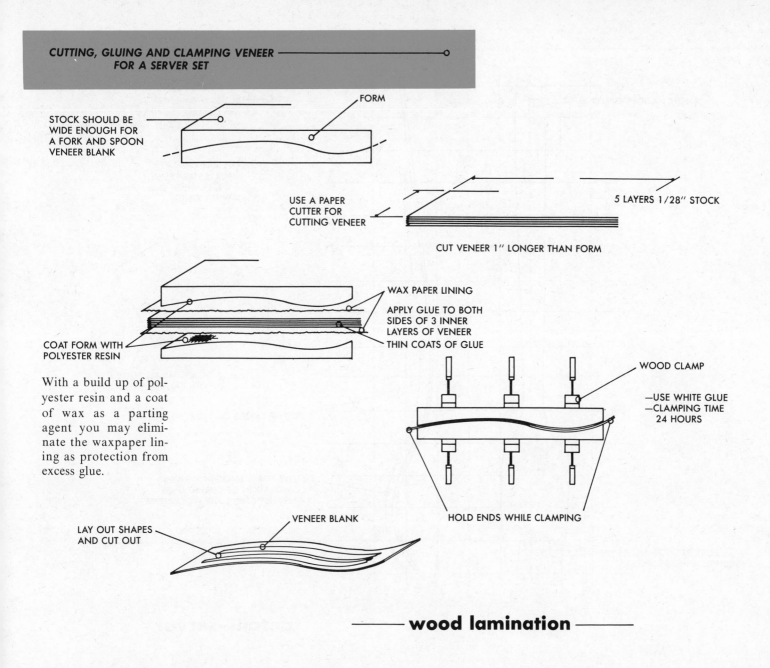

STOCK SHOULD BE
WIDE ENOUGH FOR
A FORK AND SPOON
VENEER BLANK

FORM

USE A PAPER
CUTTER FOR
CUTTING VENEER

5 LAYERS 1/28" STOCK

CUT VENEER 1" LONGER THAN FORM

WAX PAPER LINING

APPLY GLUE TO BOTH
SIDES OF 3 INNER
LAYERS OF VENEER

THIN COATS OF GLUE

COAT FORM WITH
POLYESTER RESIN

WOOD CLAMP

—USE WHITE GLUE
—CLAMPING TIME
  24 HOURS

With a build up of pol-
yester resin and a coat
of wax as a parting
agent you may elimi-
nate the waxpaper lin-
ing as protection from
excess glue.

HOLD ENDS WHILE CLAMPING

LAY OUT SHAPES
AND CUT OUT

VENEER BLANK

wood lamination

65

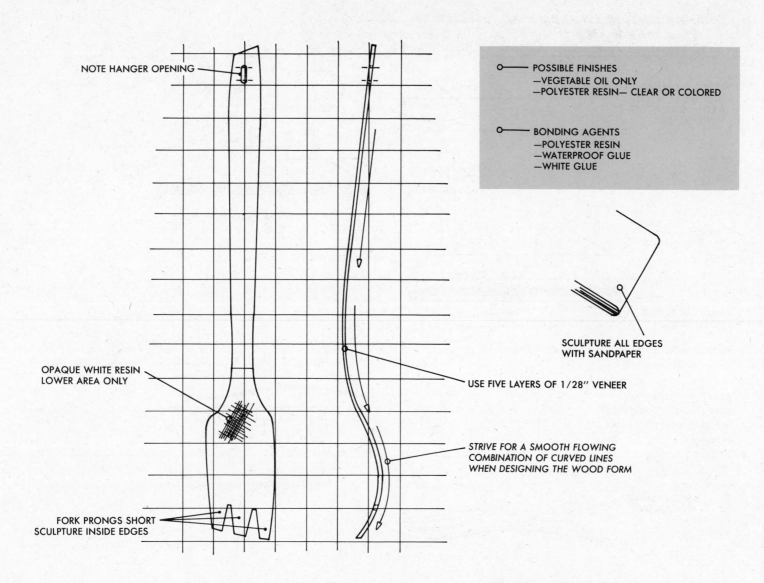

NOTE HANGER OPENING

POSSIBLE FINISHES
—VEGETABLE OIL ONLY
—POLYESTER RESIN— CLEAR OR COLORED

BONDING AGENTS
—POLYESTER RESIN
—WATERPROOF GLUE
—WHITE GLUE

SCULPTURE ALL EDGES
WITH SANDPAPER

OPAQUE WHITE RESIN
LOWER AREA ONLY

USE FIVE LAYERS OF 1/28" VENEER

STRIVE FOR A SMOOTH FLOWING
COMBINATION OF CURVED LINES
WHEN DESIGNING THE WOOD FORM

FORK PRONGS SHORT
SCULPTURE INSIDE EDGES

detail—server

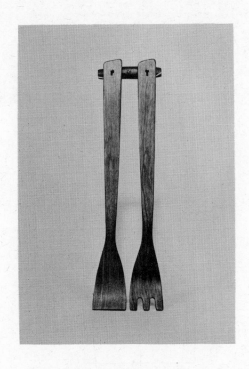

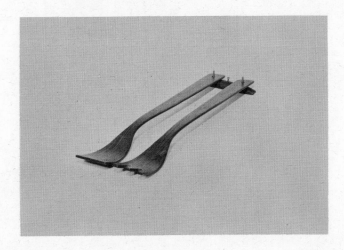

Server Set
   Note: Side profile
            Sculptured shape of hanger
            Brass hanger pegs

Server Set
   Note: Front profile shape
            Fork prongs
            Size of hanger

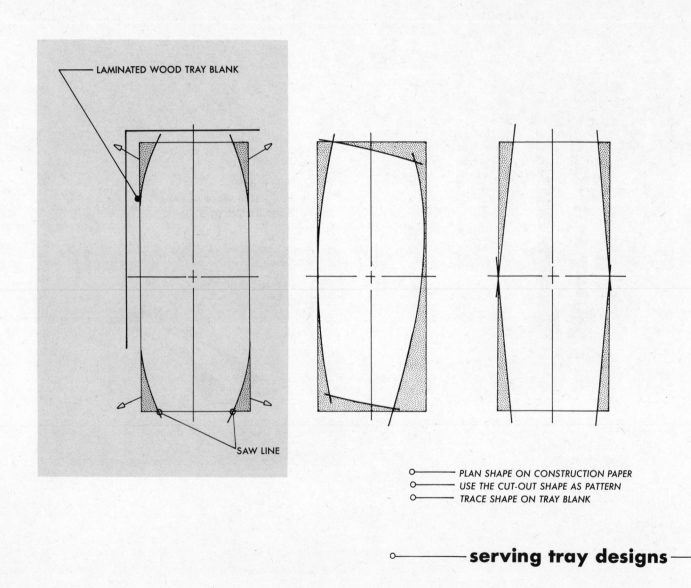

LAMINATED WOOD TRAY BLANK

SAW LINE

PLAN SHAPE ON CONSTRUCTION PAPER
USE THE CUT-OUT SHAPE AS PATTERN
TRACE SHAPE ON TRAY BLANK

serving tray designs

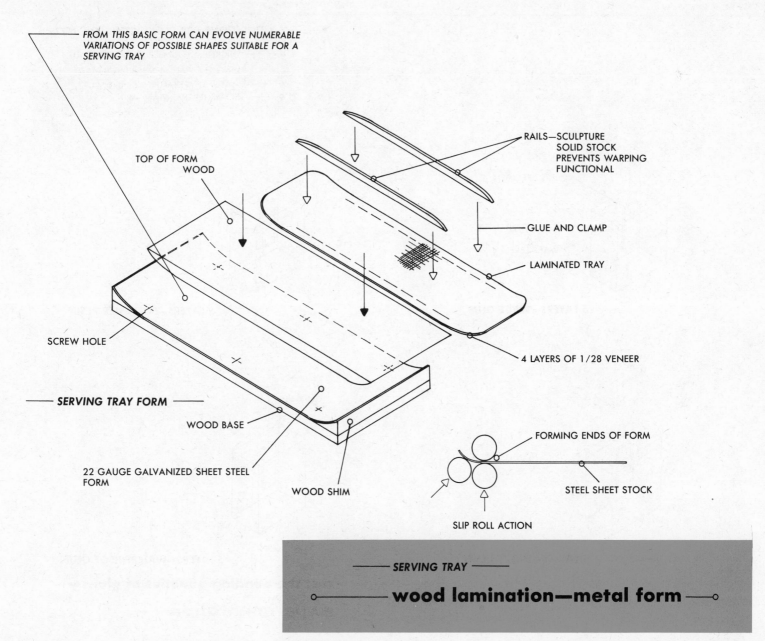

FROM THIS BASIC FORM CAN EVOLVE NUMERABLE VARIATIONS OF POSSIBLE SHAPES SUITABLE FOR A SERVING TRAY

TOP OF FORM WOOD

RAILS—SCULPTURE SOLID STOCK PREVENTS WARPING FUNCTIONAL

GLUE AND CLAMP

LAMINATED TRAY

SCREW HOLE

4 LAYERS OF 1/28 VENEER

SERVING TRAY FORM

WOOD BASE

22 GAUGE GALVANIZED SHEET STEEL FORM

WOOD SHIM

FORMING ENDS OF FORM

STEEL SHEET STOCK

SLIP ROLL ACTION

— *SERVING TRAY* —

wood lamination—metal form

69

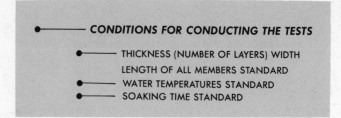
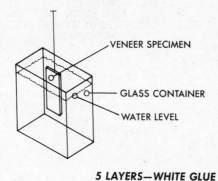

VENEER SPECIMEN

GLASS CONTAINER

WATER LEVEL

5 LAYERS—WHITE GLUE

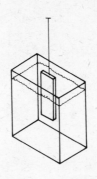

5 LAYERS—POLYESTER RESIN

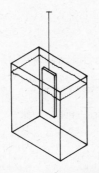

5 LAYERS—EPOXY RESIN

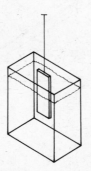

5 LAYERS—WATERPROOF GLUE

test the bonding qualities of glues—

experimentation

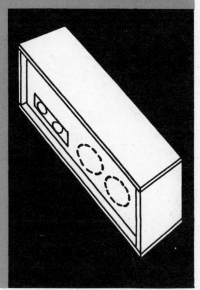

CHAPTER 4

WOOD FABRICATION
AND JOINERY

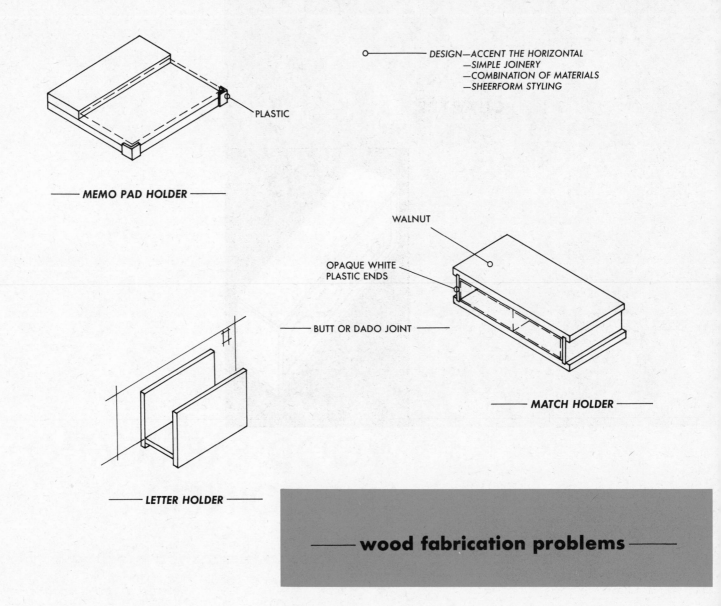

PLASTIC

— MEMO PAD HOLDER —

DESIGN—ACCENT THE HORIZONTAL
—SIMPLE JOINERY
—COMBINATION OF MATERIALS
—SHEERFORM STYLING

WALNUT

OPAQUE WHITE
PLASTIC ENDS

BUTT OR DADO JOINT

— MATCH HOLDER —

— LETTER HOLDER —

wood fabrication problems

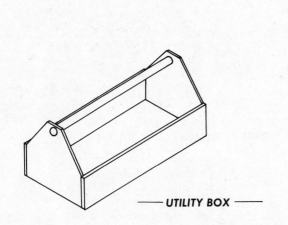

— UTILITY BOX —

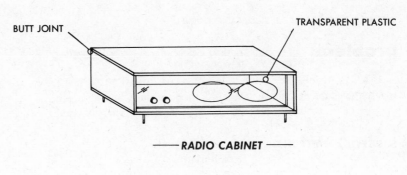

BUTT JOINT

TRANSPARENT PLASTIC

— RADIO CABINET —

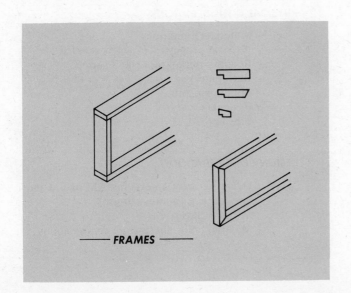

— FRAMES —

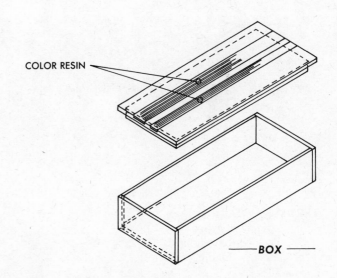

COLOR RESIN

— BOX —

wood fabrication problems

core problem: _____ *RADIO CABINET*

problem: _____ *DESIGN A RADIO CABINET FOR AN EXISTING AM OR FM UNIT*

LIMITATIONS OF PROBLEM: _ Wood, fabric (burlap), acrylic plastic, polyester resin, aluminum, plywood

SUGGESTED MATERIALS: _____ ⅜" African Teak
Red burlap

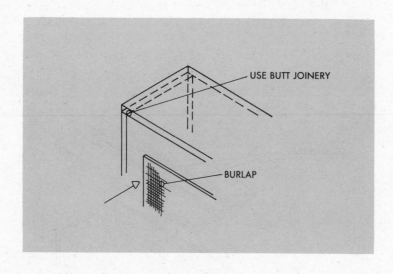

MATERIALS: ⅜" African Teak
¼" Plywood
Red burlap
Bonding agent

MATERIAL RESOURCE:
Olson Electronics, Inc.
260 S. Forge St., Akron, Ohio 44308

TOTAL PROBLEM:

1. Sketches
2. Prototype (full size)
3. Isometric drawing (full or scale size)
4. Written summary
   The written summary should be a brief statement giving the main points of the problem.

PHYSICAL CONSIDERATIONS:

Materials limitation
Physical properties of wood selected
Bonding burlap to a wood surface
Butt joinery
Bonding agents
Fasteners
Finishes

DESIGN CONSIDERATIONS:

Overall size of an existing AM or FM unit
Speaker size (number to use)
Styling—Sheerform
Material color and texture combinations

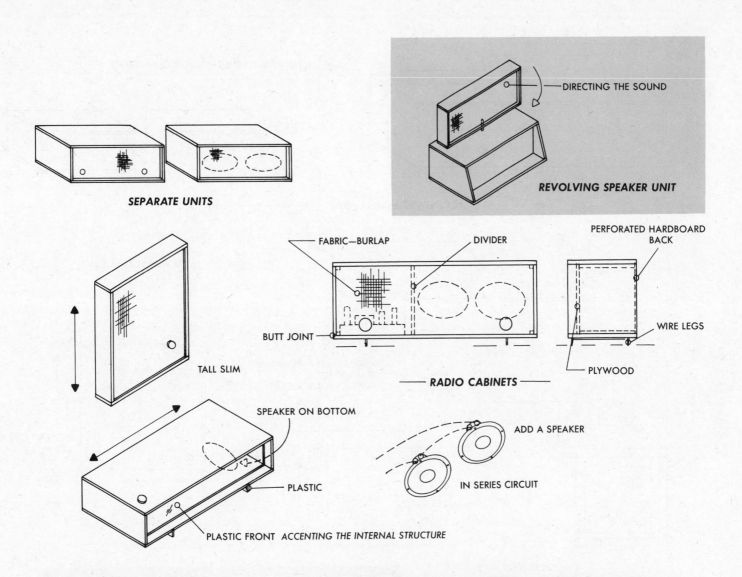

SEPARATE UNITS

DIRECTING THE SOUND

REVOLVING SPEAKER UNIT

FABRIC—BURLAP

DIVIDER

PERFORATED HARDBOARD BACK

BUTT JOINT

WIRE LEGS

PLYWOOD

RADIO CABINETS

TALL SLIM

SPEAKER ON BOTTOM

PLASTIC

ADD A SPEAKER

IN SERIES CIRCUIT

PLASTIC FRONT *ACCENTING THE INTERNAL STRUCTURE*

wood fabrication problems

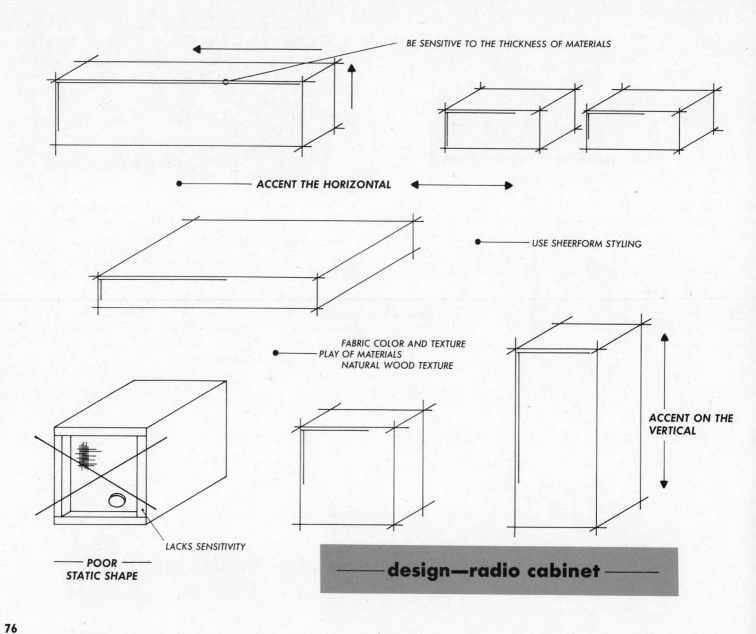

BE SENSITIVE TO THE THICKNESS OF MATERIALS

ACCENT THE HORIZONTAL

USE SHEERFORM STYLING

FABRIC COLOR AND TEXTURE
PLAY OF MATERIALS
NATURAL WOOD TEXTURE

ACCENT ON THE
VERTICAL

LACKS SENSITIVITY

POOR
STATIC SHAPE

design—radio cabinet

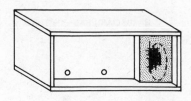

UPRIGHT OVAL SPEAKER

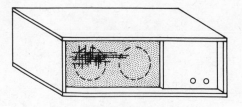

ROUND SPEAKERS

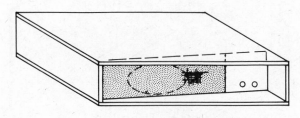

LONG OVAL SPEAKER

TWO LONG OVAL SPEAKERS

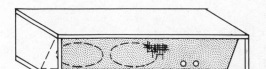

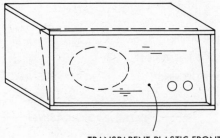

TRANSPARENT PLASTIC FRONT
TO ACCENT INTERNAL STRUCTURE
BEAUTY

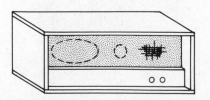

LONG OVAL SPEAKER
FOR THE LOWS AND
A SMALL ROUND
FOR THE HIGHS

front and speaker variations

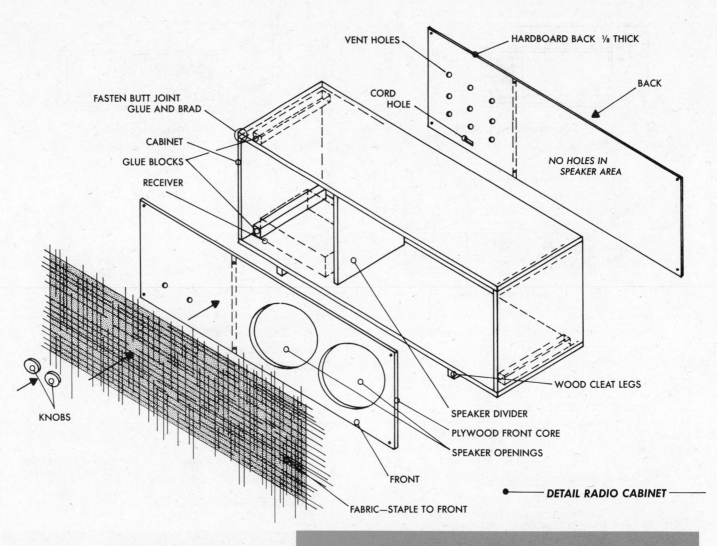

VENT HOLES

HARDBOARD BACK ⅛ THICK

BACK

FASTEN BUTT JOINT
GLUE AND BRAD

CORD
HOLE

CABINET

GLUE BLOCKS

RECEIVER

NO HOLES IN
SPEAKER AREA

WOOD CLEAT LEGS

SPEAKER DIVIDER

PLYWOOD FRONT CORE

SPEAKER OPENINGS

KNOBS

FRONT

FABRIC—STAPLE TO FRONT

DETAIL RADIO CABINET

wood fabrication problem

Front View of a Radio Cabinet

Note: Burlap front texture
Butt joinery
Wire legs and rubber tips
Accent on the horizontal

Back View of Radio Cabinet with
Backing Removed

Note: Speaker divider
Double terminal strip
Corner blocks
Receiver speaker spacing

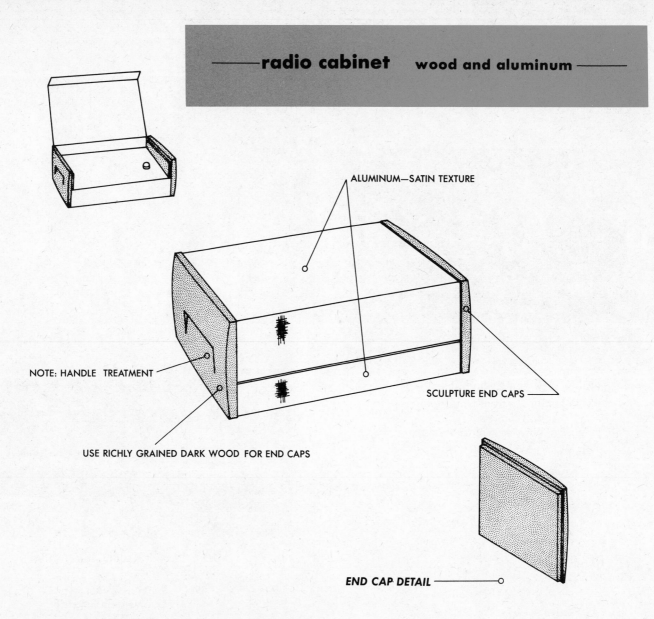

radio cabinet wood and aluminum

ALUMINUM—SATIN TEXTURE

NOTE: HANDLE TREATMENT

USE RICHLY GRAINED DARK WOOD FOR END CAPS

SCULPTURE END CAPS

END CAP DETAIL

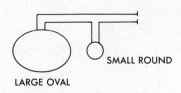

LARGE OVAL   SMALL ROUND

— **TEST AUDIO SPECTRUM** —

— **TEST FOR SOUND QUALITY
CONSIDERATIONS** —

_____ USE PM SPEAKERS (3-4 OHM VOICE COILS)
_____ ROUND SPEAKERS 4", 5", 6", 8", 10", 12"
_____ OVAL SPEAKERS 4" X 6", 5" X 7", 6" X 9"
_____ CABINET MATERIALS (SOLID STOCK, PLYWOOD, ETC.)
_____ ACOUSTIC PADDINGS (FIBERGLASS, SAND, ETC.)
_____ GRILLE MATERIALS
_____ VOLUME LEVELS
_____ WIRE IN SERIES CIRCUIT
_____ ENCLOSING SPEAKERS IN SEPARATE SOUND
          CHAMBERS TO PREVENT INTERACTION OF
          HIGH AND LOW FREQUENCIES

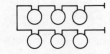

— **TEST A BANK OF SMALL ROUND SPEAKERS** —

MATERIAL RESOURCE:
          Olson Electronics, Inc.
       260 S. Forge St., Akron, Ohio 44308

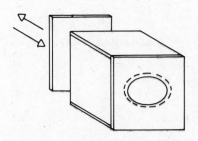

— **TEST FOR CANCELLATION EFFECTS
BETWEEN FRONT AND REAR RADIATIONS** —

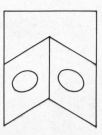

— **TEST FOR POLAR CHARACTERISTICS** —

— **speaker experimentation** —

81

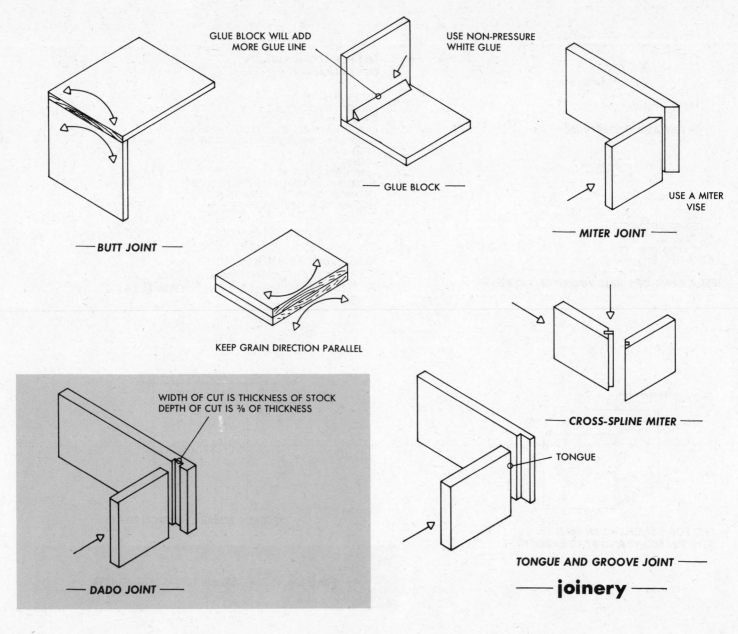

GLUE BLOCK WILL ADD
MORE GLUE LINE

USE NON-PRESSURE
WHITE GLUE

— GLUE BLOCK —

— BUTT JOINT —

KEEP GRAIN DIRECTION PARALLEL

USE A MITER
VISE

— MITER JOINT —

— CROSS-SPLINE MITER —

WIDTH OF CUT IS THICKNESS OF STOCK
DEPTH OF CUT IS ⅜ OF THICKNESS

— DADO JOINT —

TONGUE

TONGUE AND GROOVE JOINT —

— joinery —

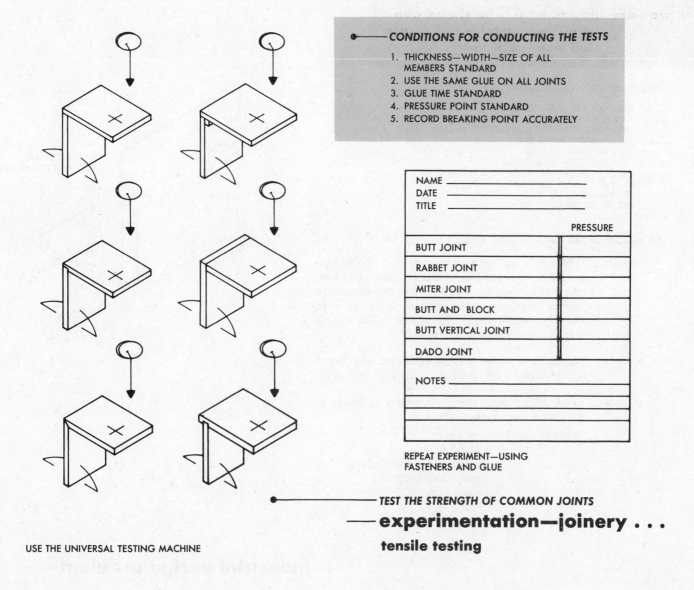

NAME _____
DATE _____
TITLE _____

	PRESSURE
BUTT JOINT	
RABBET JOINT	
MITER JOINT	
BUTT AND BLOCK	
BUTT VERTICAL JOINT	
DADO JOINT	
NOTES _____	

REPEAT EXPERIMENT—USING FASTENERS AND GLUE

TEST THE STRENGTH OF COMMON JOINTS

experimentation—joinery . . .

tensile testing

USE THE UNIVERSAL TESTING MACHINE

CONSIDERATIONS AND LIMITATIONS

_____ CASE SIZE 9½" X 5⅞" X 2⅞"
_____ WILL BE MANUFACTURED OF HIGH-IMPACT PLASTIC
_____ MUST HAVE A HANDLE, CAN DOUBLE AS LEG
_____ ILLUMINATED TUNING DIAL
_____ 3 X 5 IN. OVAL SPEAKER
_____ ONE TELESCOPING ANTENNA
_____ BATTERY POWER ONLY (3 "D" SIZE FLASHLIGHT)
_____ BATTERIES CAN BE CHANGED WITHOUT TAKING
CASE APART COMPLETELY
_____ USE WOOD OR CLAY FOR MOCK-UP

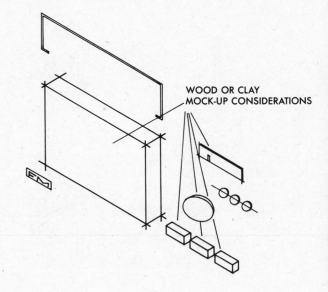

WOOD OR CLAY
MOCK-UP CONSIDERATIONS

THE DESIGN OF THE CASE SHOULD REFLECT

ORDER ____ ORDER is the methodic disposition of elements according to a definite system. Housings and handles, buttons and knobs, grille and ventilation slots, seams, inserts, switches, dials, surfaces and edges should be methodically disposed according to a system of alignments and parallels.

HARMONY _ Harmony in design is the special kind of order in which all parts are made to agree, creating a unity.

ECONOMY _ Economy is the creation of harmony in design by the fewest and simplest means.

Avoid using . . . ornaments
emblems
embossed and recessed effects
overhangs and undercuts
unnecessary doors or frames
fake veneers, etc.

—industrial design problem—

84

CHAPTER 5

WOOD TURNING

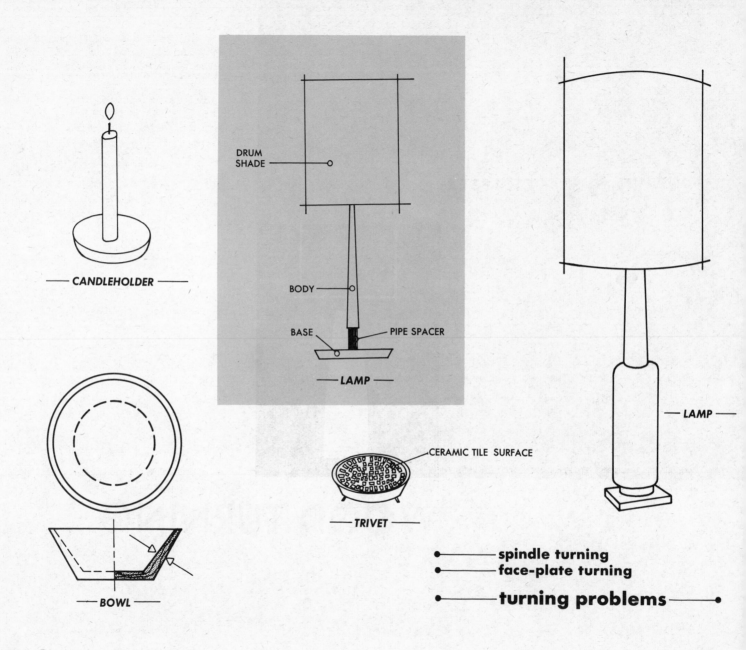

CANDLEHOLDER

DRUM SHADE

BODY

BASE

PIPE SPACER

LAMP

BOWL

CERAMIC TILE SURFACE

TRIVET

LAMP

● spindle turning
● face-plate turning

● **turning problems**

86

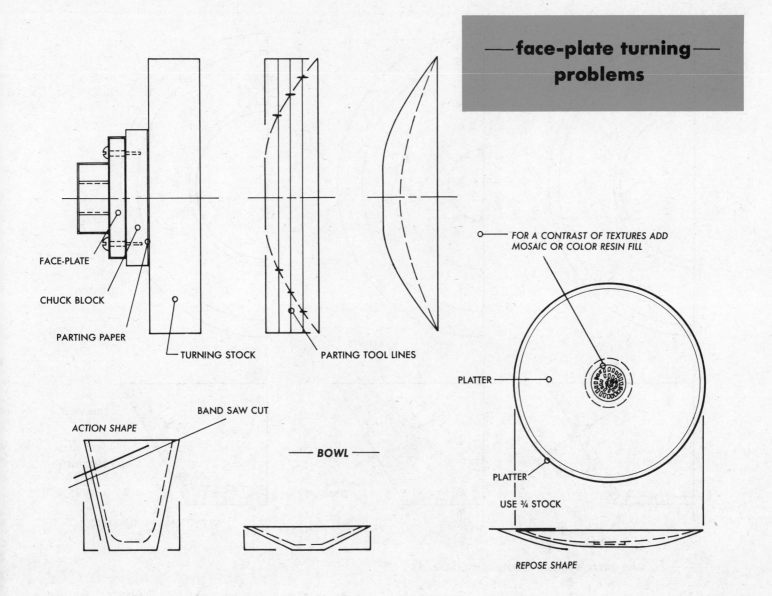

FACE-PLATE

CHUCK BLOCK

PARTING PAPER

TURNING STOCK

PARTING TOOL LINES

FOR A CONTRAST OF TEXTURES ADD MOSAIC OR COLOR RESIN FILL

PLATTER

PLATTER

USE ¾ STOCK

ACTION SHAPE

BAND SAW CUT

—BOWL—

REPOSE SHAPE

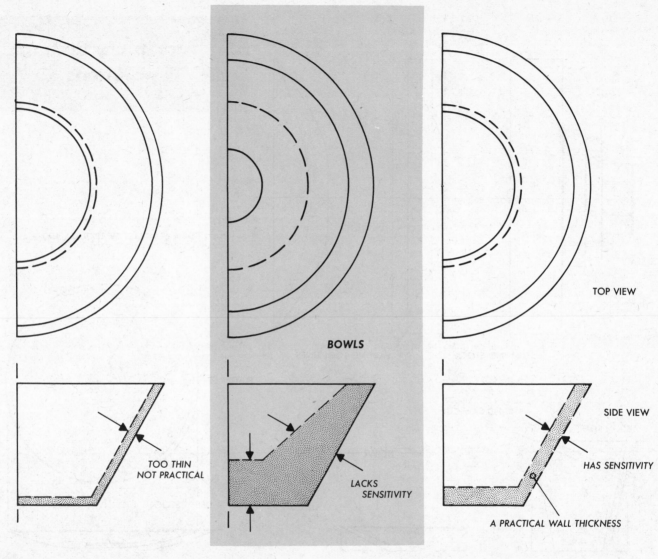

CONCAVE SURFACES SHOULD FOLLOW CONVEX SURFACES

BOWLS

TOP VIEW

SIDE VIEW

TOO THIN
NOT PRACTICAL

LACKS
SENSITIVITY

HAS SENSITIVITY

A PRACTICAL WALL THICKNESS

turning—wall thickness and sensitivity

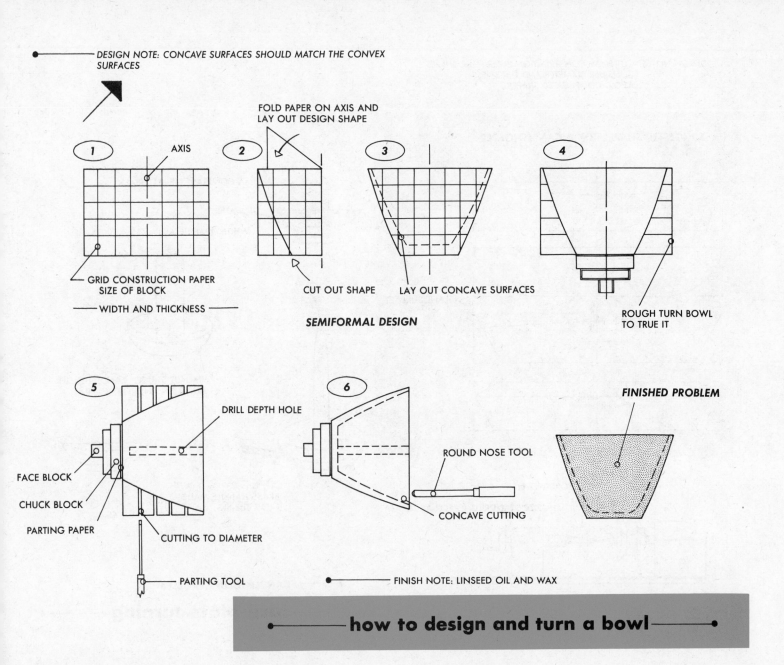

DESIGN NOTE: CONCAVE SURFACES SHOULD MATCH THE CONVEX SURFACES

1 AXIS

GRID CONSTRUCTION PAPER SIZE OF BLOCK

WIDTH AND THICKNESS

2 FOLD PAPER ON AXIS AND LAY OUT DESIGN SHAPE

CUT OUT SHAPE

3 LAY OUT CONCAVE SURFACES

4 ROUGH TURN BOWL TO TRUE IT

SEMIFORMAL DESIGN

5 DRILL DEPTH HOLE

FACE BLOCK

CHUCK BLOCK

PARTING PAPER

CUTTING TO DIAMETER

PARTING TOOL

6 ROUND NOSE TOOL

CONCAVE CUTTING

FINISHED PROBLEM

FINISH NOTE: LINSEED OIL AND WAX

how to design and turn a bowl

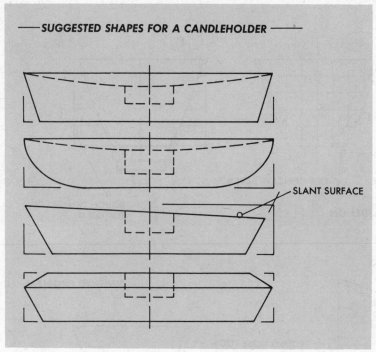

— SUGGESTED SHAPES FOR A CANDLEHOLDER —

SLANT SURFACE

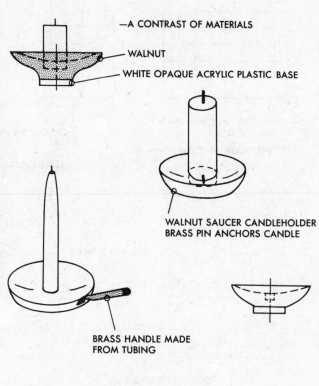

—A CONTRAST OF MATERIALS

WALNUT

WHITE OPAQUE ACRYLIC PLASTIC BASE

WALNUT SAUCER CANDLEHOLDER
BRASS PIN ANCHORS CANDLE

BRASS HANDLE MADE
FROM TUBING

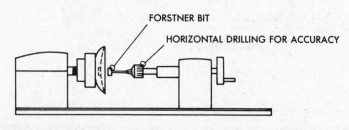

FORSTNER BIT

HORIZONTAL DRILLING FOR ACCURACY

CANDLEHOLDER PROBLEM

face-plate turning

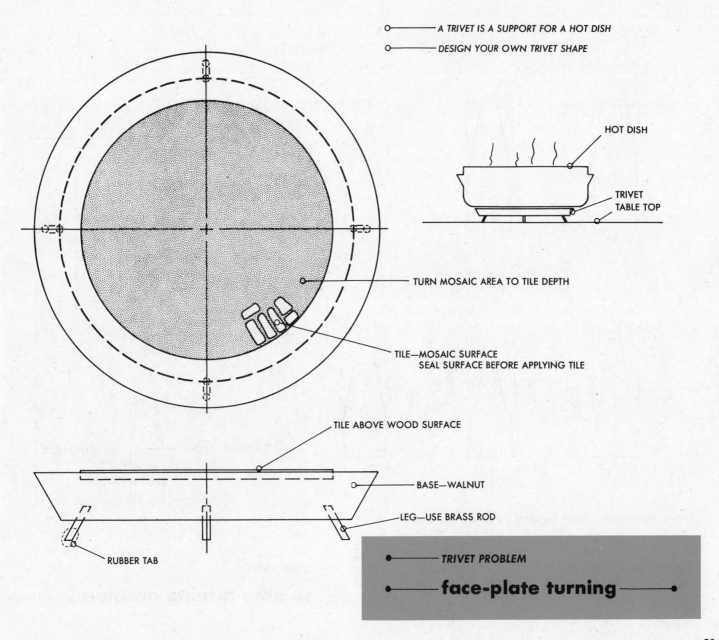

A TRIVET IS A SUPPORT FOR A HOT DISH

DESIGN YOUR OWN TRIVET SHAPE

HOT DISH

TRIVET
TABLE TOP

TURN MOSAIC AREA TO TILE DEPTH

TILE—MOSAIC SURFACE
SEAL SURFACE BEFORE APPLYING TILE

TILE ABOVE WOOD SURFACE

BASE—WALNUT

LEG—USE BRASS ROD

RUBBER TAB

TRIVET PROBLEM

face-plate turning

91

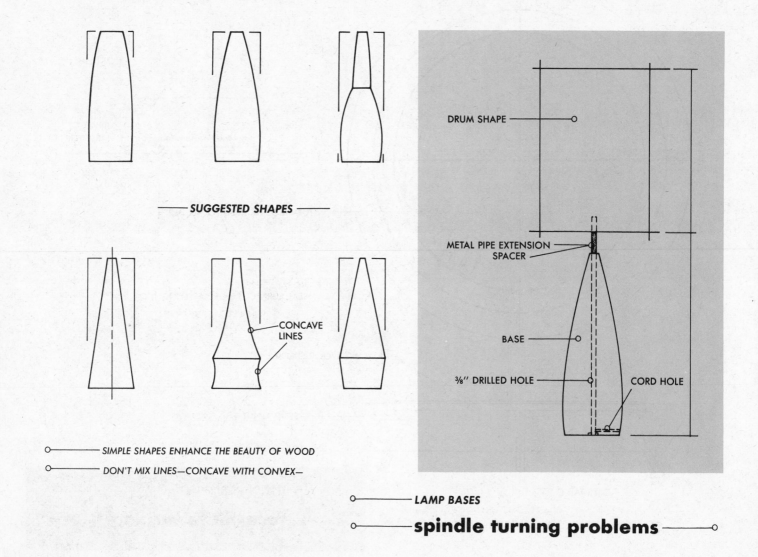

— SUGGESTED SHAPES —

CONCAVE
LINES

DRUM SHAPE

METAL PIPE EXTENSION
SPACER

BASE

⅜" DRILLED HOLE

CORD HOLE

— SIMPLE SHAPES ENHANCE THE BEAUTY OF WOOD

— DON'T MIX LINES—CONCAVE WITH CONVEX—

— LAMP BASES

spindle turning problems

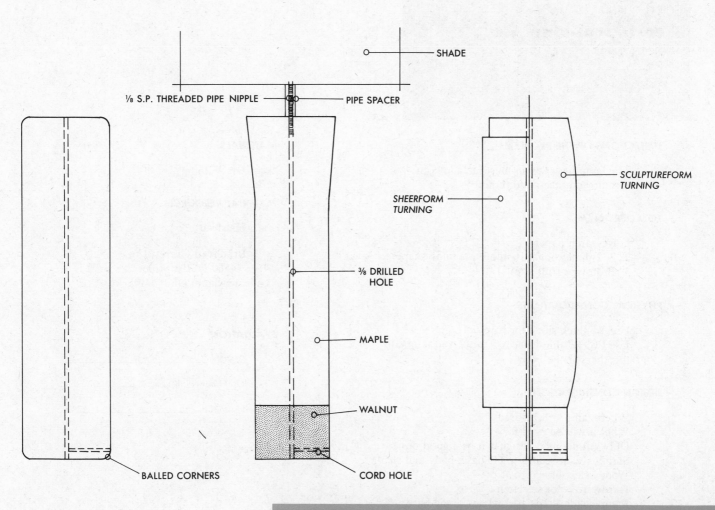

SHADE

⅛ S.P. THREADED PIPE NIPPLE — PIPE SPACER

SCULPTUREFORM
TURNING

SHEERFORM
TURNING

⅜ DRILLED
HOLE

MAPLE

WALNUT

BALLED CORNERS

CORD HOLE

LAMP BASES

spindle turning problems

core problem: LAMP

problem: *DESIGN A TURNED LAMP BASE*

LIMITATIONS OF THE PROBLEM:

The lamp base design must include both
spindle and face-plate turning

TOTAL PROBLEM:

1. Research paper
2. 3, 2-dimensional stand-up planning shapes
3. Prototype (full size)

PHYSICAL CONSIDERATIONS:

Use ¾″ thick stock for base
Use two ¾″ thick pieces of stock and laminate
together for the body

DESIGN CONSIDERATIONS:

Where lamp will be used
What it will be used for
Only a functional design can be a good design
Stability as it relates to the base, body and shade
Wood selection
Hardware color selection
Lamp shade shape as it relates to the base
STYLING—SCULPTUREFORM or SHEERFORM

MATERIALS:

¾″ Walnut

MATERIAL RESOURCE:

Hardware

Brodhead-Garrett Co.
4560 E. 71st Street
Cleveland, Ohio 44105

EVALUATION:

DESIGN _____

CRAFTSMANSHIP _____

RESEARCH _____

If you are going to execute a turning problem, this lamp combination is worthy of consideration because

- —unlimited design possibilities
- —the use of ¾″ stock cuts costs
- —includes both spindle and face-plate turning experiences
- —can be a small or large lamp design

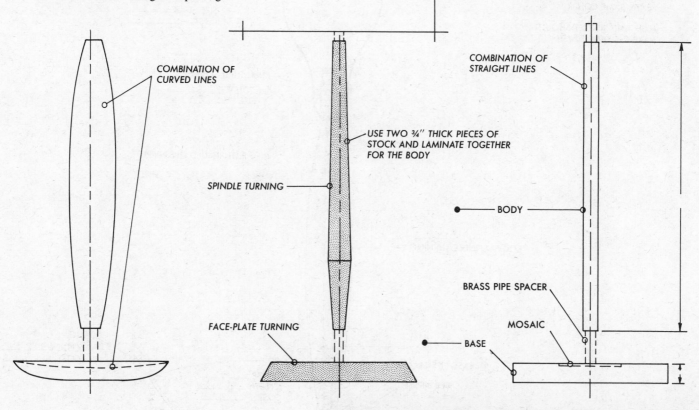

COMBINATION OF CURVED LINES

COMBINATION OF STRAIGHT LINES

USE TWO ¾″ THICK PIECES OF STOCK AND LAMINATE TOGETHER FOR THE BODY

SPINDLE TURNING

BODY

BRASS PIPE SPACER

MOSAIC

FACE-PLATE TURNING

BASE

● ——— LAMP VARIATIONS

● ——— **turning problem** ———●

95

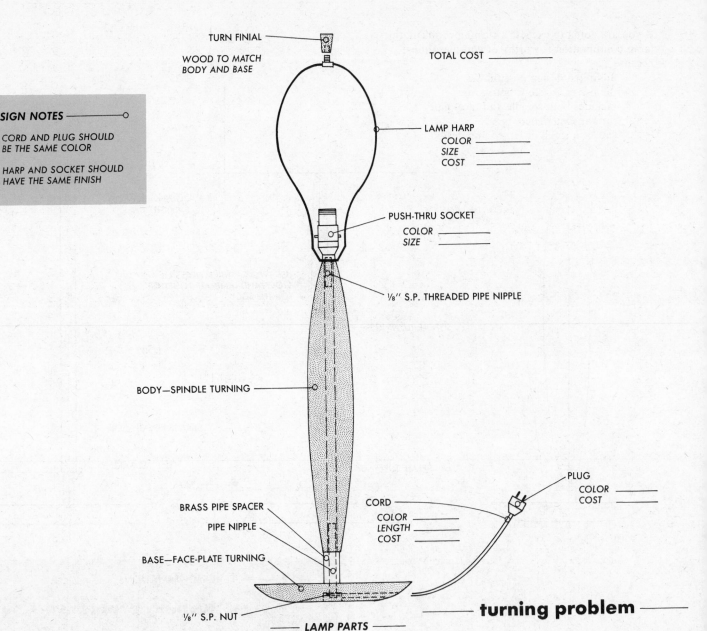

TURN FINIAL

WOOD TO MATCH
BODY AND BASE

TOTAL COST _____

DESIGN NOTES ———————o

CORD AND PLUG SHOULD
BE THE SAME COLOR

HARP AND SOCKET SHOULD
HAVE THE SAME FINISH

LAMP HARP
COLOR _____
SIZE _____
COST _____

PUSH-THRU SOCKET

COLOR _____
SIZE _____

⅛" S.P. THREADED PIPE NIPPLE

BODY—SPINDLE TURNING

PLUG
COLOR _____
COST _____

CORD

COLOR _____
LENGTH _____
COST _____

BRASS PIPE SPACER

PIPE NIPPLE

BASE—FACE-PLATE TURNING

⅛" S.P. NUT

LAMP PARTS

turning problem

96

Lamp
  Note: Spindle turning body
        Face-plate turning base
        Mosaic inlay on base
        Metal spacers
        Drum shade
        Base and shade size relation

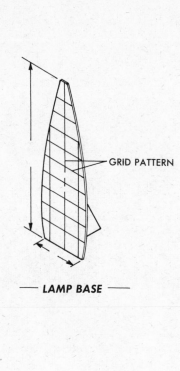

GRID PATTERN

— LAMP BASE —

PLANNING TECHNIQUE

—FOR A QUICK AND ACCURATE CONCEPT OF
  A TURNING SHAPE
—GRID 4-PLY POSTER BOARD
—LAY OUT SHAPE FULL SIZE
—CUT OUT AND PROP UP WITH A TAB
—3-DIMENSIONAL EFFECT
—SHAPES MUST BE SYMMETRICAL
—USE BROWN POSTER BOARD TO HELP SIMULATE WOOD

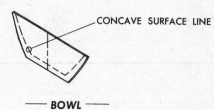

CONCAVE SURFACE LINE

— BOWL —

— CANDLEHOLDER —

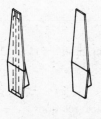

— SHAKERS —

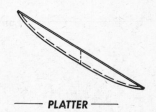

— PLATTER —

— TRIVET —

design technique
2-dimensional stand-up shapes
turning shapes

98

Candle Holder
  Note: Spindle turning body
        Plain candle
        Candle base size relation

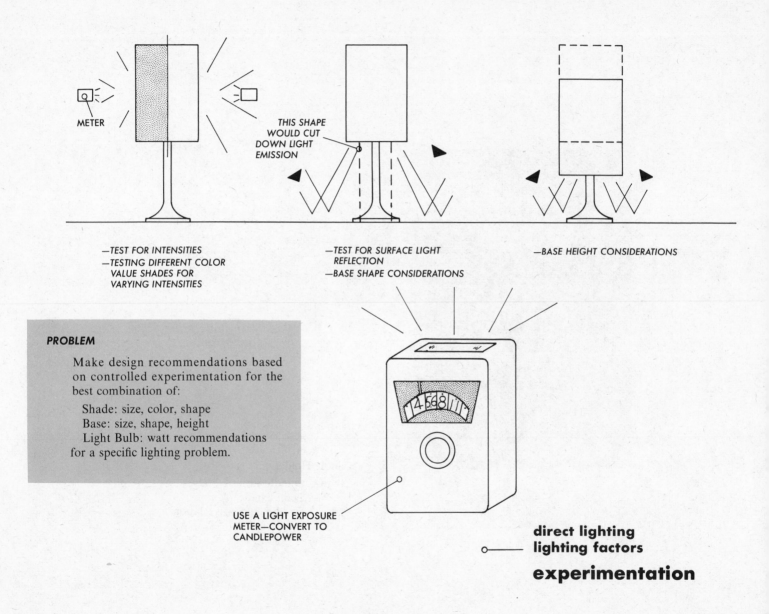

METER

—TEST FOR INTENSITIES
—TESTING DIFFERENT COLOR
   VALUE SHADES FOR
   VARYING INTENSITIES

THIS SHAPE
WOULD CUT
DOWN LIGHT
EMISSION

—TEST FOR SURFACE LIGHT
   REFLECTION
—BASE SHAPE CONSIDERATIONS

—BASE HEIGHT CONSIDERATIONS

PROBLEM

Make design recommendations based on controlled experimentation for the best combination of:

Shade: size, color, shape
Base: size, shape, height
Light Bulb: watt recommendations for a specific lighting problem.

USE A LIGHT EXPOSURE
METER—CONVERT TO
CANDLEPOWER

**direct lighting
lighting factors**

experimentation

CHAPTER 6

PLASTICS

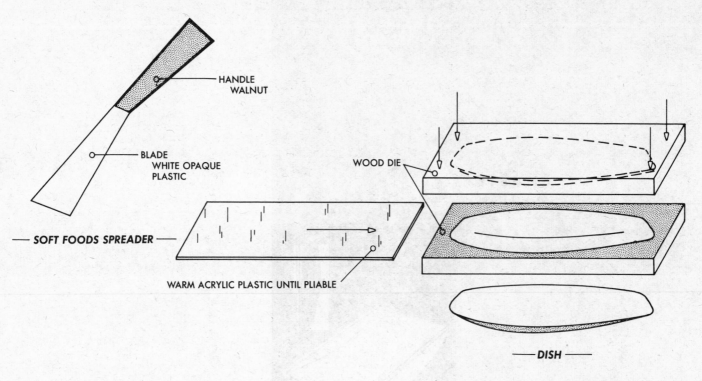

HANDLE
WALNUT

BLADE
WHITE OPAQUE
PLASTIC

— SOFT FOODS SPREADER —

WARM ACRYLIC PLASTIC UNTIL PLIABLE

WOOD DIE

— DISH —

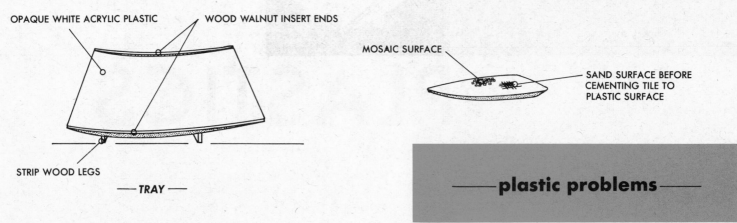

OPAQUE WHITE ACRYLIC PLASTIC

WOOD WALNUT INSERT ENDS

MOSAIC SURFACE

SAND SURFACE BEFORE
CEMENTING TILE TO
PLASTIC SURFACE

STRIP WOOD LEGS

— TRAY —

— plastic problems —

102

problem: *SOFT FOODS SPREADER*

core problem: *DESIGN A SOFT FOODS SPREADER*

LIMITATIONS OF PROBLEM:

Use wood and acrylic plastic in your solution

SUGGESTED MATERIALS:

⅛″ White opaque acrylic plastic
¼″ Walnut

TOTAL PROBLEM:

1. Sketches
2. Template
3. Prototype (full size)
4. Drawing (multiview)
5. Written summary
   The written summary should be a brief statement giving the main points of the problem.

PHYSICAL CONSIDERATIONS:

Materials limitation
Physical properties of acrylic plastic
Suitable bonding agent
Physical properties of walnut
Finish

DESIGN CONSIDERATIONS:

Rid yourself of spreader stereotypes
Consider what a spreader must do
Only a functional design can be good design
Color of plastic
Color of walnut
Styling—SCULPTUREFORM or SHEERFORM

The design for a spreader, as well as everything else,
must fulfill three basic functions:

1. Mechanical function
2. Physical function
3. Psychological function

MECHANICAL FUNCTION

Blade considerations
a. Thickness, b. Edge treatment,
c. Compound angles

PHYSICAL FUNCTION

Handle
a. Balance, b. "Feel" considerations

PSYCHOLOGICAL FUNCTION

Looks
a. Grasp by looks, b. Strength of blade by look,
c. Blade handle relation

MATERIALS:

⅛″ White opaque acrylic plastic
¼″ Walnut
   Bonding agent

MATERIAL RESOURCE:

Cadillac Plastic Company
   15111 Second Avenue
   Detroit 3, Michigan

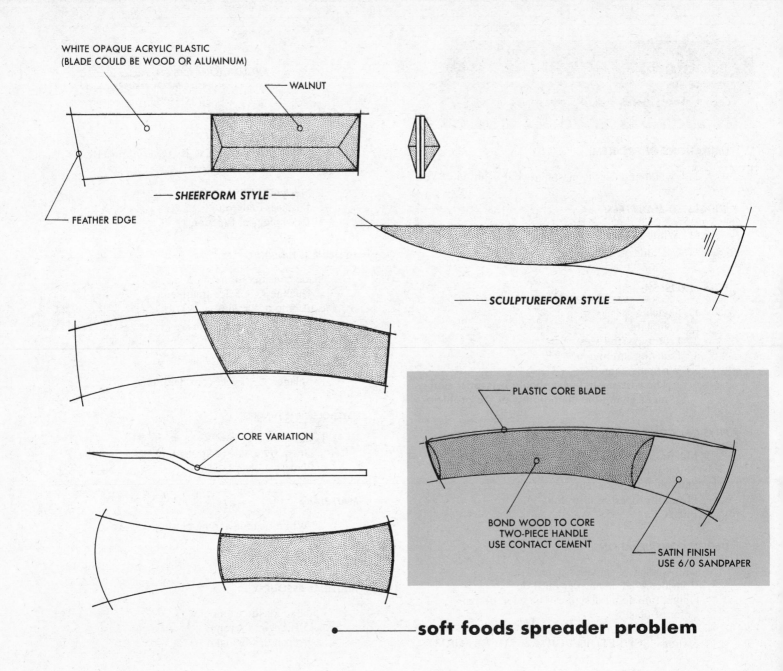

WHITE OPAQUE ACRYLIC PLASTIC
(BLADE COULD BE WOOD OR ALUMINUM)

WALNUT

SHEERFORM STYLE

FEATHER EDGE

SCULPTUREFORM STYLE

CORE VARIATION

PLASTIC CORE BLADE

BOND WOOD TO CORE
TWO-PIECE HANDLE
USE CONTACT CEMENT

SATIN FINISH
USE 6/0 SANDPAPER

soft foods spreader problem

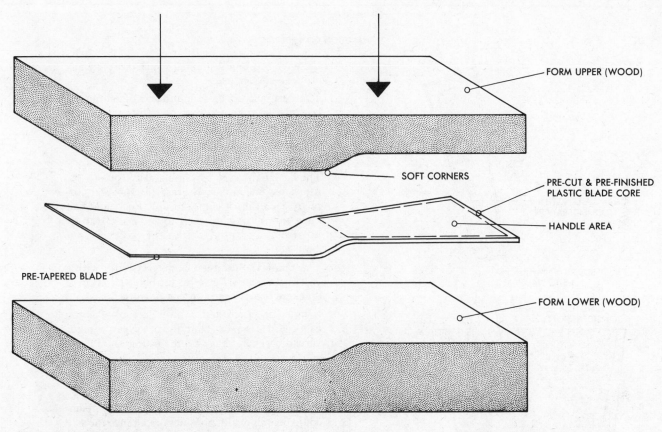

FORM UPPER (WOOD)

SOFT CORNERS

PRE-CUT & PRE-FINISHED
PLASTIC BLADE CORE

HANDLE AREA

PRE-TAPERED BLADE

FORM LOWER (WOOD)

TO VARY BLADE CORE PROFILE

CHOOSE A HARD CLOSED GRAIN
WOOD FOR THE FORM

Design a two-part form with the profile you desire; pre-heat finished shaped plastic until it becomes pliable; place plastic in the form and apply pressure; let plastic cool and remove from form; bond wood to handle area.

DON'T—overheat plastic
    —apply too much pressure

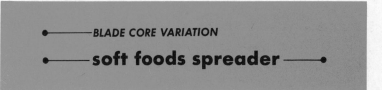

BLADE CORE VARIATION

soft foods spreader

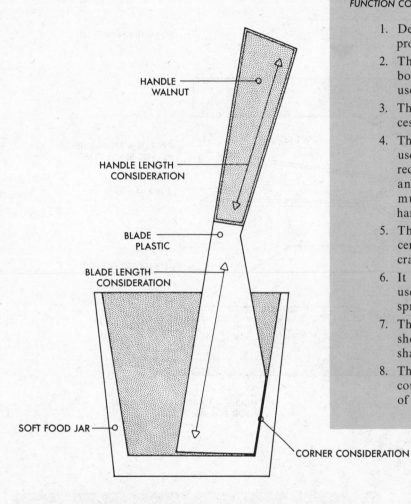

HANDLE
WALNUT

HANDLE LENGTH
CONSIDERATION

BLADE
PLASTIC

BLADE LENGTH
CONSIDERATION

SOFT FOOD JAR

CORNER CONSIDERATION

1. Design a soft foods spreader which is esthetically prone to kitchen use.

2. The design must be functional in reaching the bottom of most containers, thereby enabling the user to obtain all of the contents.

3. The spreader must be easy to clean with no recessed areas for food to lodge in.

4. The design must be psychologically sound—the user must unconsciously grasp the spreader correctly each time it is picked up. "Feel" and balance should be conveyed to the user. Handle must be long enough to fit the palm of your hand.

5. The blade should have slight flexibility with a certain amount of "give" as the blade passes over crackers if it is used for this purpose.

6. It must be functional, a kitchen tool of many uses—dip from a container; spread bread; spread crackers; have some cutting ability.

7. The design must be contemporary, sensitive and should have clean flowing surfaces with no sharp lines.

8. The design should be one that a food company could economically promote to enhance the sale of their product.

soft foods spreader

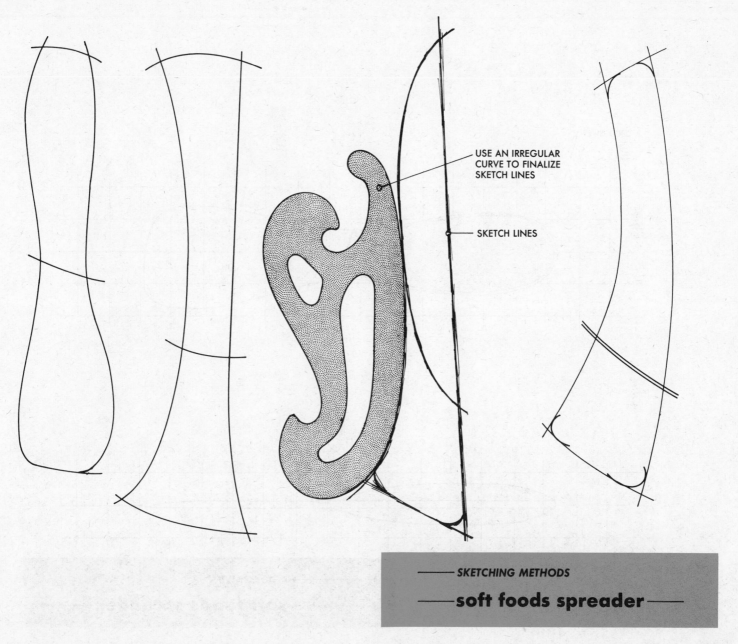

USE AN IRREGULAR
CURVE TO FINALIZE
SKETCH LINES

SKETCH LINES

SKETCHING METHODS
soft foods spreader

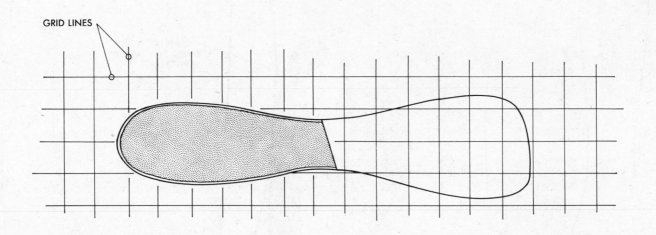

GRID LINES

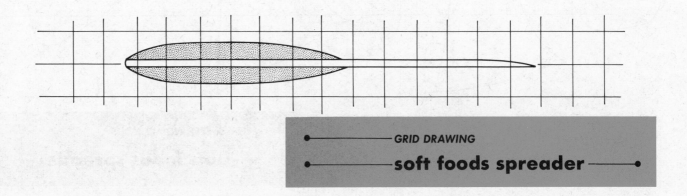

GRID DRAWING
soft foods spreader

Soft Food Spreader
  Note: Shape
           Plastic wood combination

Soft Food Spreader in a Use Situation

REMOVE MIRROR FINISH ON PLASTIC HANDLE AREA
WITH SANDPAPER BEFORE APPLYING BONDING AGENT

ROUGH HANDLE AREA
WITH SANDPAPER

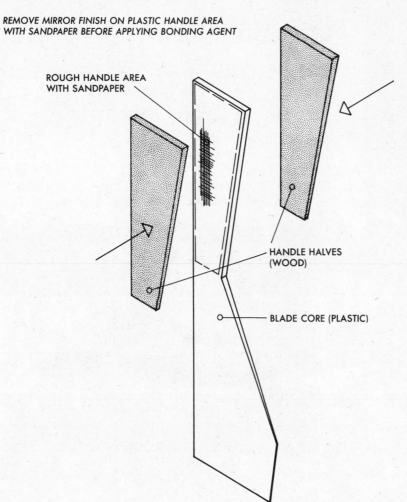

HANDLE HALVES
(WOOD)

BLADE CORE (PLASTIC)

TEST THE HOLDING POWER OF THE FOLLOWING BONDING AGENTS

1. CONTACT CEMENT
2. WHITE GLUE
3. EPOXY GLUE
4. POLYESTER RESIN

*TEST SHEAR ON A UNIVERSAL TESTING MACHINE
EQUIPMENT RESOURCE:*

Brodhead-Garrett Co.
4560 E. 71st Street
Cleveland, Ohio 44105

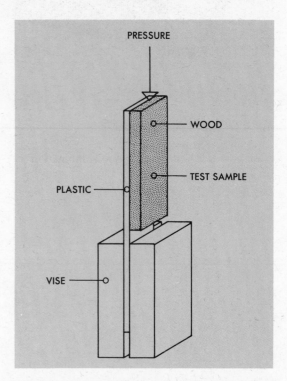

PRESSURE

WOOD

TEST SAMPLE

PLASTIC

VISE

TEST THE HOLDING PROPERTIES OF DIFFERENT BONDING AGENTS

experimentation

CHAPTER 7

FIBER GLASS

Plastics reinforced with glass fiber are being used for a wide variety of industrial products such as model boat hulls, chair forms, and lamp parts.

Glass fiber combined with plastic resin (polyester or epoxy) forms a structural material that is stronger in proportion to its weight than any commonly used materials. Its use is continuing to expand rapidly because of a unique combination of properties unequalled in any other industrial material.

STRENGTH
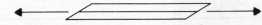

The tensile strength of glass fiber filaments is over 200,000 *psi. Combined with resin, glass fiber fabrics offer high weight-strength ratio and tremendous impact strength.

DURABILITY

Chemically stable, glass fiber will not rot, mildew or oxidize. It is unaffected by acids (except hydrofluoric and hot phosphoric) or by weak alkalies.

DIMENSIONAL STABILITY

Glass fiber will not shrink or stretch in processing.

HEAT RESISTANCE
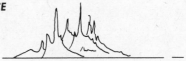

Glass fiber will withstand varying temperatures up to 1000° F.

MOISTURE RESISTANCE

Glass fiber cannot absorb moisture beyond surface wetting.

*psi—Pounds per square inch

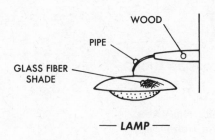

WOOD

PIPE

GLASS FIBER
SHADE

— LAMP —

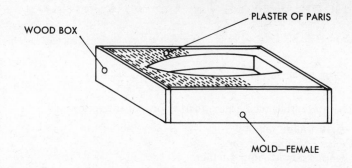

WOOD BOX

PLASTER OF PARIS

MOLD—FEMALE

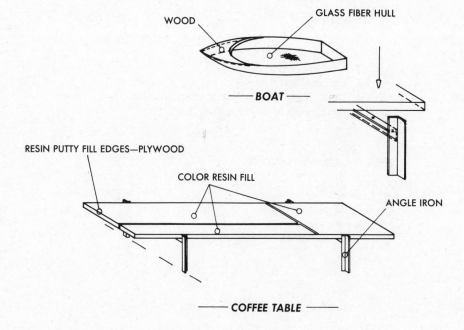

WOOD

GLASS FIBER HULL

— BOAT —

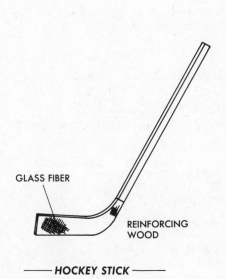

GLASS FIBER

REINFORCING
WOOD

— HOCKEY STICK —

RESIN PUTTY FILL EDGES—PLYWOOD

COLOR RESIN FILL

ANGLE IRON

— COFFEE TABLE —

core problem: *A GLASS FIBER BOAT HULL*

problem: *DESIGN A BOAT MOLD OR FORM AND EXECUTE A HULL IN GLASS FIBER*

LIMITATIONS OF PROBLEM:

The glass fiber technique must be one of the following:

Sock Forming Method
Contact Molding Method
Compression Molding Method

TOTAL PROBLEM:

1. Design mold or form
2. Construct mold or form
3. Execute boat hull
4. Design and construct deck superstructure
5. Install sails or power unit

PHYSICAL CONSIDERATIONS:

Glass fiber limitations
Size (scale or full)
Cost
Hull must float correctly

DESIGN CONSIDERATIONS:

Use
Single Hull Design
Twin Hull Design
Speed
Hydrofoil Principles

EMPHASIS:

Marine research on boat hull design
Glass fiber process

MATERIAL RESOURCE:

Cadillac Plastic Company
Detroit 3, Michigan, 15111 Second Avenue

EVALUATION:

DESIGN ＿＿＿＿＿＿＿

CRAFTSMANSHIP ＿＿＿＿＿

RESEARCH ＿＿＿＿＿＿＿

SOCK FORMING

—SIMPLE BOTH IN METHOD AND MAKING FORM
—ONE MALE RIB FORM
—STRETCHING MATERIAL OVER FORM

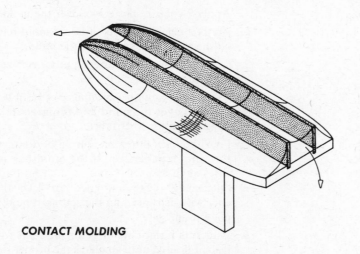

CONTACT MOLDING

—MORE COMPLEX IN METHOD AND MAKING MOLD
—ONE FEMALE OR MALE PLASTER OR GLASS FIBER MOLD
—NO PRESSURE USED IN LAYING UP MATERIAL

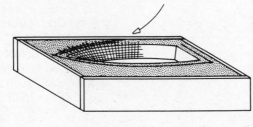

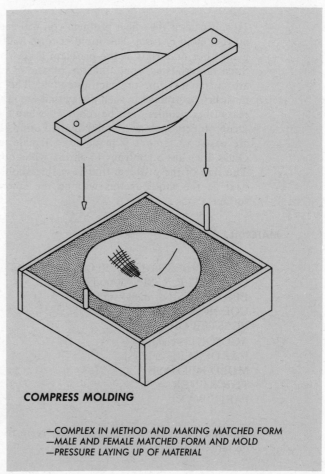

COMPRESS MOLDING

—COMPLEX IN METHOD AND MAKING MATCHED FORM
—MALE AND FEMALE MATCHED FORM AND MOLD
—PRESSURE LAYING UP OF MATERIAL

•— three methods to form and mold glass fiber —•

the glass fiber technique ————————●

contact molding ————————————————●

To construct a glass fiber problem you will need to make a mold or form. This mold or form holds the glass fiber materials as the problem takes shape. Such materials as wood, plaster, plastic or metal are satisfactory for constructing a mold. The mold must be constructed in such a way that the molded glass fiber problem can be removed when cured. Deep objects such as a bullet-shaped lamp shade are easier to remove if made on a female mold. Glass fiber has a tendency to shrink when curing. The side of the problem that is visible should be next to the mold as this will be the smoother surface.

MATERIALS ————————————●

GLASS FIBER FABRIC, 10 OZ. UNTREATED
POLYESTER RESIN—wood surface
EPOXY RESIN—metal surfaces
COLOR PIGMENT
PLASTER OF PARIS
ACETONE—cleaning
HARDENER—catalyst
MOLD RELEASE
THICKENER
PASTE WAX

Epoxy resin is superior to polyester resin for use on large problems.

MOLDING OPERATIONS ————————●

1. Apply 2 coats of paste wax over the mold.

2. Apply 2 generous coats of liquid mold release on the paste wax surface of the mold.

3. Cut the glass fiber fabric slightly oversize for the mold surface.

4. Estimate the number of ounces of resin it will take to cover the mold and impregnate and cover the glass fiber fabric.

5. Pour the resin into a measuring bottle then in turn into a paper cup. If the mold has steep sides such as a boat hull, you should add a thickener so the resin will not "run." The thickener will also speed up the setting time of applied resin.

6. Add small amounts of color pigment to the resin if desired until you have the proper shade and stir thoroughly. If too much pigment is added to the resin the solution will not set-up when applied to a surface.

7. Add hardener and stir thoroughly. USE ¼ TEASPOON OF HARDENER PER OUNCE OF RESIN AT A TEMPERATURE OF ABOUT 70°F. (polyester resin). If you find this sets up too fast, decrease the hardener. You will have about 10 to 20 minutes after adding the hardener until it is no longer workable.

8. Brush on a generous amount of mixed resin on the mold surface. Allow this resin coat to become tacky. Apply another liberal resin coat to the mold surface and lay the glass fiber fabric on the resin-coated mold surface and work out the AIR between the mold and the glass fiber. The tacky coat of resin on the mold surface will prevent the glass fiber coming directly in contact with the mold surface. This step should guarantee a smooth surface with no sanding needed. MAKE SURE THE GLASS FIBER IS IN FULL CONTACT WITH THE MOLD SURFACES.

9. Apply more resin over the glass fiber fabric. You may allow this coat to become tacky and apply more resin and glass fiber fabric or allow it to harden and cure and continue at a later time.

10. Allow the problem to cure for about one hour and then release the form from the mold while it is still pliable. After the release place the form back into the mold. After a 12-hour set-up time in the mold, remove the form and sand if needed.

   AVOID PROLONGED BREATHING OF THE VAPORS GIVEN OFF BY THE RESIN. AVOID APPLYING IN A CLOSED ROOM. USE THE SAME SAFETY PRECAUTIONS FOR ACETONE AND RESINS AS YOU WOULD LACQUER THINNER OR OTHER SIMILAR SOLVENTS IN THE INDUSTRIAL ARTS AREA. DO NOT STORE THE RESINS IN DIRECT SUNLIGHT OR NEAR ANY TYPE OF HEAT. DO NOT ALLOW TO FREEZE.

Reinforced plastics made by contact molding require only the pressure of contact. The mold is a single piece and can be made of plaster, wood, metal, plastic, or sand. Glass fiber fabric is laid in the mold. It is then catalyzed, and accelerated resin is painted, sprayed, or poured on the glass, and the air is worked out by brushing or rolling. In contact molding, the finish of the reinforced part not in contact with the mold will not be of the highest quality, since no pressure is applied in the operation.

Contact molding is probably the most economical way to produce one, or a small number of reinforced plastic parts, no matter how large or how small the part.

BOAT HULL ———————————●

1 ONLY A FEMALE MOLD IS USED FOR THIS GLASS FIBER REINFORCED PLASTICS MODEL BOAT HULL. THE INSIDE OF THE HULL DOES NOT REQUIRE A FINISHED SURFACE.

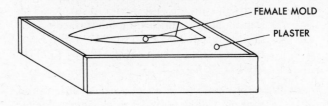

— FEMALE MOLD

— PLASTER

2 THE LAY-UP OF GLASS FIBER FABRIC IS IMPREGNATED WITH THE MIXED RESIN IN THE MOLD.

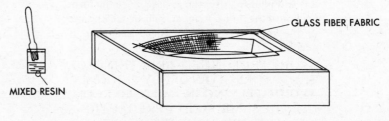

GLASS FIBER FABRIC

MIXED RESIN

3 AFTER A PRESCRIBED CURING PERIOD AT ROOM TEMPERATURE, THE LIGHT, STRONG BOAT HULL CAN BE LIFTED OUT OF THE MOLD.

4 TRIM AND SAND EDGES—ADD WOOD DECK AND POWER.

● —— ONLY ONE FEMALE MOLD NEEDED
● —— NO PRESSURE EXCEPT CONTACT
● —— MOST ECONOMICAL WAY TO PRODUCE A FEW PROBLEMS
● —— POLYESTER RESIN REINFORCED WITH GLASS FIBER

—— **glass fiber fabrication** contact molding ——

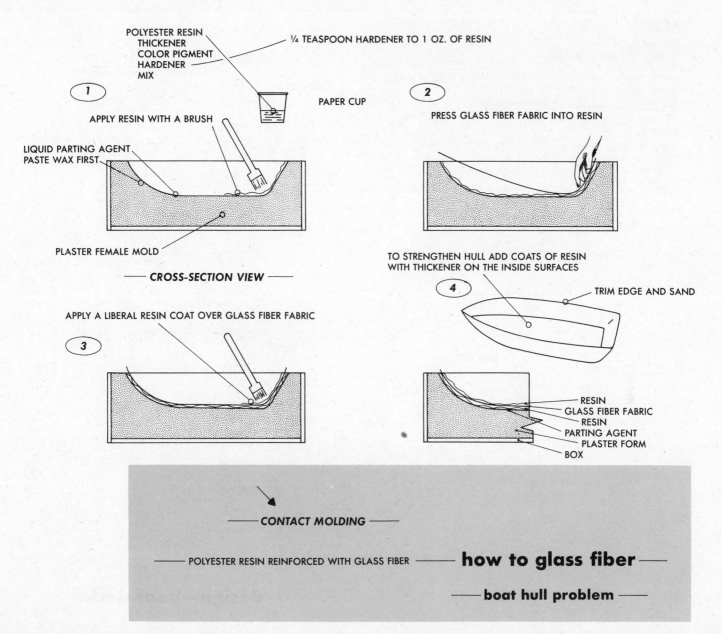

1. POLYESTER RESIN
THICKENER
COLOR PIGMENT
HARDENER
MIX

¼ TEASPOON HARDENER TO 1 OZ. OF RESIN

PAPER CUP

APPLY RESIN WITH A BRUSH

LIQUID PARTING AGENT
PASTE WAX FIRST

PLASTER FEMALE MOLD

— CROSS-SECTION VIEW —

2. PRESS GLASS FIBER FABRIC INTO RESIN

3. APPLY A LIBERAL RESIN COAT OVER GLASS FIBER FABRIC

TO STRENGTHEN HULL ADD COATS OF RESIN
WITH THICKENER ON THE INSIDE SURFACES

4. TRIM EDGE AND SAND

RESIN
GLASS FIBER FABRIC
RESIN
PARTING AGENT
PLASTER FORM
BOX

— CONTACT MOLDING —

—— POLYESTER RESIN REINFORCED WITH GLASS FIBER —— **how to glass fiber**——

—— **boat hull problem** ——

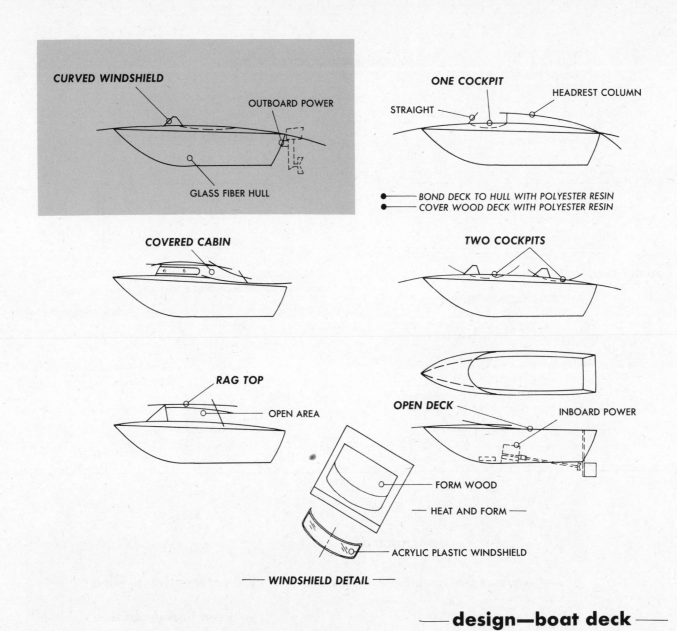

CURVED WINDSHIELD

OUTBOARD POWER

GLASS FIBER HULL

ONE COCKPIT

STRAIGHT

HEADREST COLUMN

● ⎯⎯ BOND DECK TO HULL WITH POLYESTER RESIN
● ⎯⎯ COVER WOOD DECK WITH POLYESTER RESIN

COVERED CABIN

TWO COCKPITS

RAG TOP

OPEN AREA

OPEN DECK

INBOARD POWER

FORM WOOD

⎯ HEAT AND FORM ⎯

ACRYLIC PLASTIC WINDSHIELD

⎯ WINDSHIELD DETAIL ⎯

design—boat deck

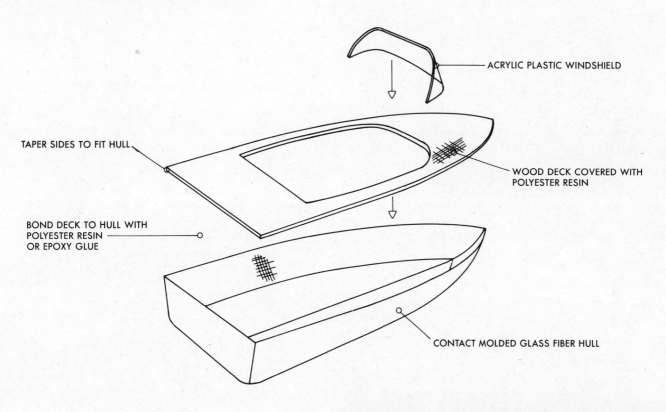

USE INBOARD OR OUTBOARD POWER

ACRYLIC PLASTIC WINDSHIELD

TAPER SIDES TO FIT HULL

WOOD DECK COVERED WITH
POLYESTER RESIN

BOND DECK TO HULL WITH
POLYESTER RESIN
OR EPOXY GLUE

CONTACT MOLDED GLASS FIBER HULL

DETAIL BOAT

glass fiber problem

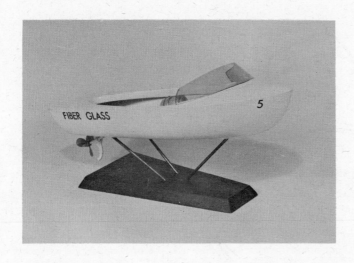

Contact Molded Boat

   Note: Curved plastic windshield
           Power unit
           Base

sock forming ──────────●

For quick and inexpensive shapes made of glass fiber the SOCK FORMING METHOD is the answer. The student should be able to design and construct a simple form with little difficulty. Forms can be made from scrap hardboard and plywood.

FORMING OPERATIONS ──────────●

1. Design and make a rib form.
2. Place form in a vise.
3. Run masking tape along all leading bearing edges of ribs and base shape. Masking tape will act as the parting factor.
4. Stretch and staple a soft, clean T-shirt cotton cloth over the male ribbed form.
5. Estimate the number of ounces of resin it will take to cover the form.
6. Pour the resin into a measuring bottle then in turn into a paper cup. To add strength to the cotton fabric add a thickener to the resin.
7. Add small amounts of color pigment to the resin if desired until you have the proper shade and stir thoroughly. If too much pigment is added to the resin, the solution will not set-up when applied to a surface.
8. Add hardener and stir thoroughly. USE ¼ TEASPOON OF HARDENER PER OUNCE OF RESIN AT A TEMPERATURE OF ABOUT 70°F. for polyester resin. If you find this sets up too fast, decrease the hardener. You will have about 10 to 20 minutes after adding the hardener until the solution is no longer workable.
9. Brush on a generous amount of mixed resin on the stretched cotton cloth formed surface. Build-up several coats.
10. If the sock shape is large, apply a layer of glass fiber fabric to reinforce built-up thickener resin coats.
11. To remove the sock shape from the form, score a line with the backsaw in center of the edge of base shape.
12. Remove shape, sand and spray paint.

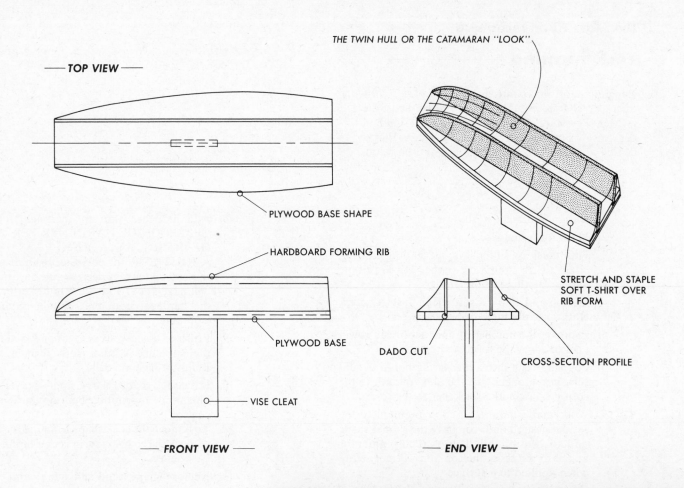

— *TOP VIEW* —

THE TWIN HULL OR THE CATAMARAN "LOOK"

PLYWOOD BASE SHAPE

HARDBOARD FORMING RIB

PLYWOOD BASE

STRETCH AND STAPLE
SOFT T-SHIRT OVER
RIB FORM

VISE CLEAT

DADO CUT

CROSS-SECTION PROFILE

— *FRONT VIEW* —

— *END VIEW* —

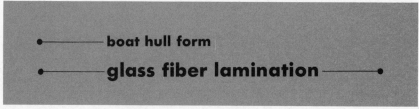

- boat hull form
- # glass fiber lamination

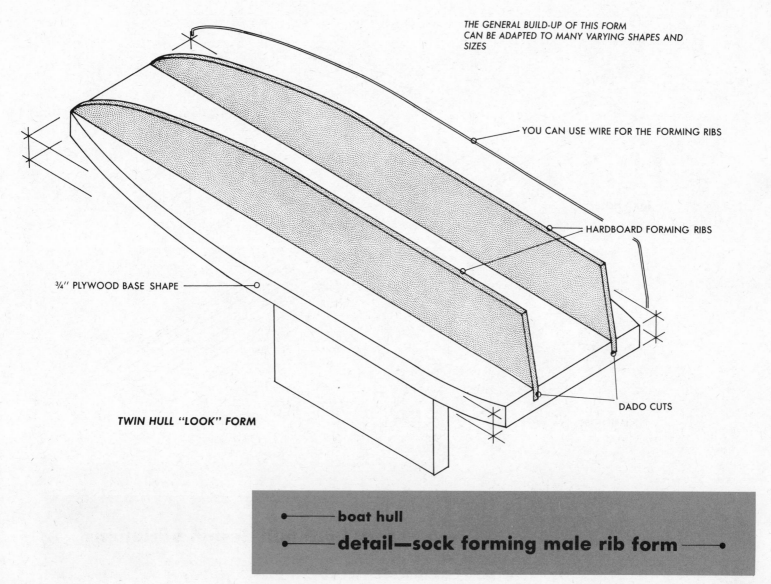

THE GENERAL BUILD-UP OF THIS FORM
CAN BE ADAPTED TO MANY VARYING SHAPES AND
SIZES

YOU CAN USE WIRE FOR THE FORMING RIBS

HARDBOARD FORMING RIBS

¾'' PLYWOOD BASE SHAPE

DADO CUTS

TWIN HULL "LOOK" FORM

boat hull

detail—sock forming male rib form

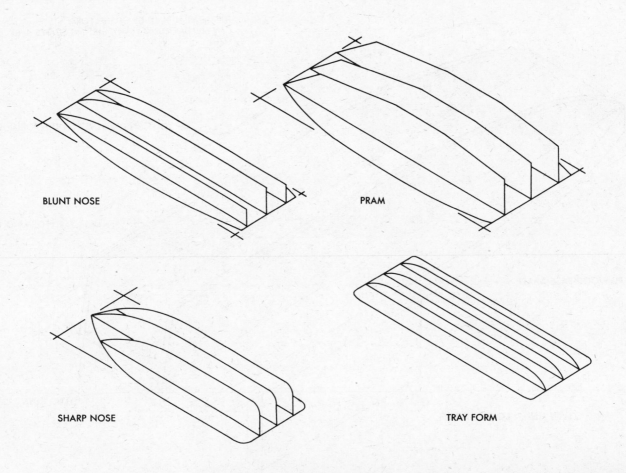

BLUNT NOSE

PRAM

SHARP NOSE

TRAY FORM

sock boat hull design variations

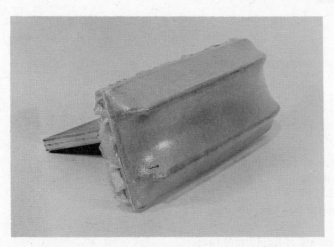

Sock Boat Hull Form Before Removing Hull Shape

Note: Stapled surplus material around base
of form
Scored saw line

Sock Boat Hull Form with Hull Shape Removed

Note: Bottom view
Hardboard ribs

the glass fiber technique

compression molding

Compression molding is the most complex method for glass fiber shapes. The two factors that make it worth your consideration are:

Your glass fiber product will have an inside and outside smooth finished surface.

It will eliminate air pockets between the mold, glass fiber fabric and form.

MOLDING OPERATIONS

1. Design a compression female mold and male form. Take in consideration the wall thickness of the glass fiber shape desired.

2. Apply 2 coats of paste wax over the mold and form.

3. Apply 2 generous coats of liquid mold release on the paste wax surface of the mold and form.

4. Follow steps 3, 4, 5, 6 and 7 under contact molding.

5. Brush on a generous amount of mixed resin on the female mold and male form. Allow these resin coats to become tacky. Apply another liberal resin coat to the mold surface and lay the glass fiber fabric on the resin-coated mold surface and work in by hand. Now apply a generous resin coat over the glass fiber fabric and place male form in position with pressure.

6. Allow the problem to cure for about one hour and a half, then release the form from the mold and remove the shape. After the release, place the shape back into the mold and replace form. After a 12-hour set-up time in the mold with the form in place under pressure, remove the shape and sand if needed.

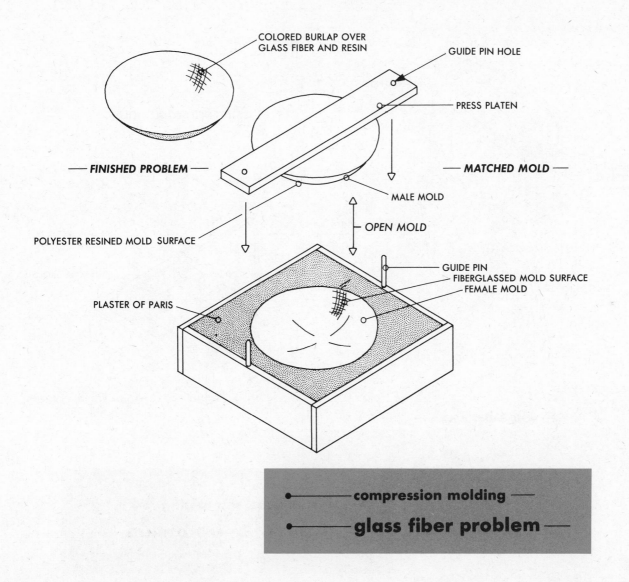

COLORED BURLAP OVER
GLASS FIBER AND RESIN

GUIDE PIN HOLE

PRESS PLATEN

— *FINISHED PROBLEM* —

— *MATCHED MOLD* —

MALE MOLD

POLYESTER RESINED MOLD SURFACE

OPEN MOLD

GUIDE PIN

FIBERGLASSED MOLD SURFACE

FEMALE MOLD

PLASTER OF PARIS

— compression molding —

— **glass fiber problem** —

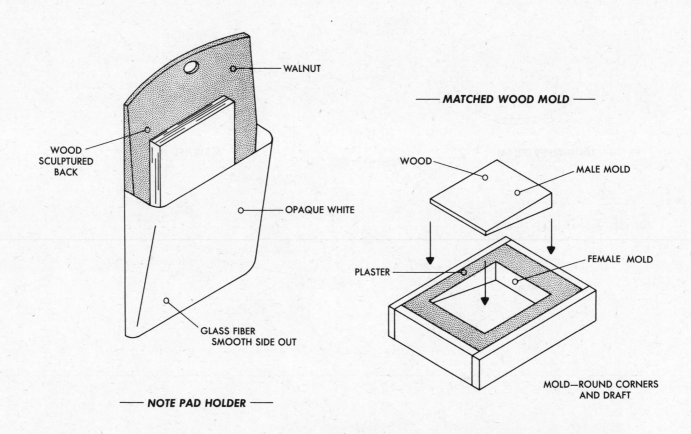

WALNUT

WOOD
SCULPTURED
BACK

OPAQUE WHITE

GLASS FIBER
SMOOTH SIDE OUT

NOTE PAD HOLDER

— *MATCHED WOOD MOLD* —

WOOD

MALE MOLD

PLASTER

FEMALE MOLD

MOLD—ROUND CORNERS
AND DRAFT

— compression molding
— **glass fiber problem** —

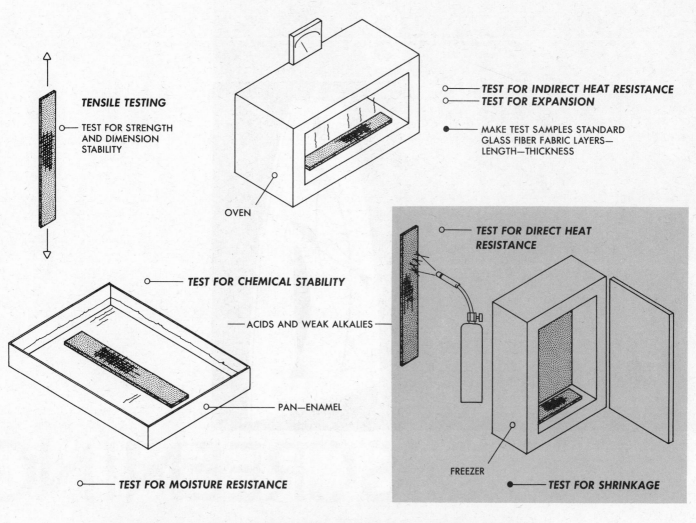

TENSILE TESTING

○── TEST FOR STRENGTH
AND DIMENSION
STABILITY

OVEN

○── TEST FOR INDIRECT HEAT RESISTANCE
○── TEST FOR EXPANSION

●── MAKE TEST SAMPLES STANDARD
GLASS FIBER FABRIC LAYERS—
LENGTH—THICKNESS

○── TEST FOR CHEMICAL STABILITY

── ACIDS AND WEAK ALKALIES

── PAN—ENAMEL

○── TEST FOR MOISTURE RESISTANCE

○── TEST FOR DIRECT HEAT
RESISTANCE

FREEZER

●── TEST FOR SHRINKAGE

○── **test the properties of glass fiber as plastics reinforcements**

●── **experimentation—glass fiber** ──

CHAPTER 8

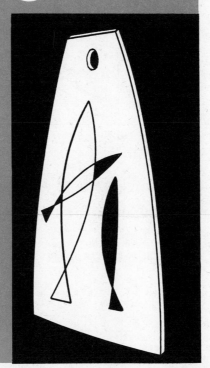

SCREENING

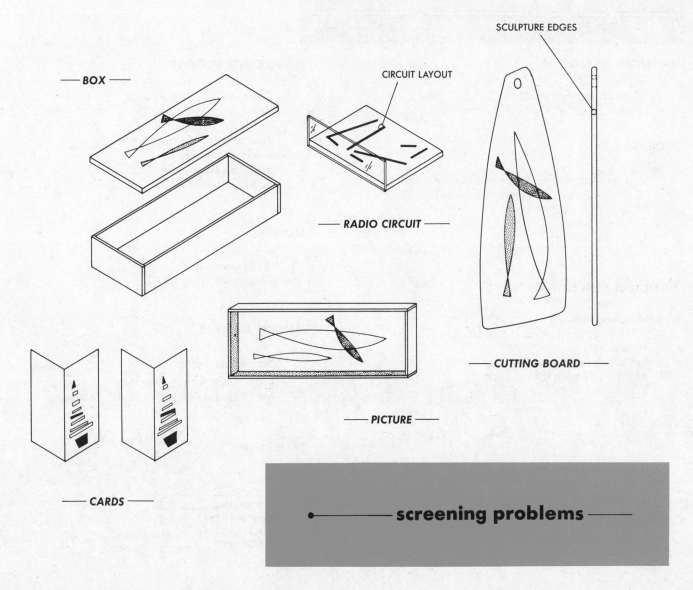

BOX

CIRCUIT LAYOUT

SCULPTURE EDGES

RADIO CIRCUIT

CUTTING BOARD

PICTURE

CARDS

screening problems

133

core problem: CUTTING BOARD PLAQUE

problem: DESIGN A CUTTING BOARD PLAQUE SHAPE AND SCREEN STENCIL

LIMITATIONS OF PROBLEM:

⅜″ maple or birch wood

TOTAL PROBLEM:

1. 4 full-size, construction paper cutting board shapes. Select one design to execute
2. Prototype (full size)
3. Screen stencil
4. Screen prototype

PHYSICAL CONSIDERATIONS:

Material limitation
   Maple or birch physical properties
Hanger hole
Finish—cutting board
Finish—screening ink (enamel)

DESIGN CONSIDERATIONS:

Color of cutting board wood
Color of screening inks
Sensitivity of material
Hanger hole shape and size
Cutting board shape
Screening shapes and format
STYLING—Sculpture form

MATERIAL:

⅜″ Maple or birch
Enamel screening inks

MATERIAL RESOURCE:

Screening supplies
Lewis Artist Supply Company
6408 Woodward Ave., Detroit 2, Michigan

EVALUATION:

DESIGN
   PLAQUE _____
   SCREENING _____
CRAFTSMANSHIP
   PLAQUE _____
   SCREENING _____

the screening technique

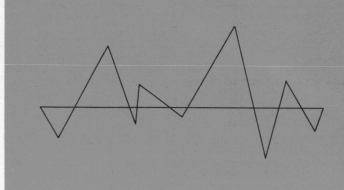

Screening technique printing as an activity in industrial arts design problems is a relatively new and simple process. It joins with many other methods of two-dimensional reproduction such as stenciling and block printing.

The basic principle of the screen technique is to force color through a fine meshed fabric. The greatest advantage of the screen technique is the low cost of plate reproduction.

The screen technique is known under other names such as silk screen process, mitography and screen stenciling.

Advantages of the screening technique

1. COLOR

Because of the density of the pigment, light colors, even white, can be solidly printed over dark surfaces.

2. LOW COST

A screen stencil can be prepared inexpensively since it is essentially handwork. Perfect art work or "copy" is not required; minor corrections and changes can be made easily as the stencil is cut.

3. VERSATILITY

Screen prints on nearly any surface: paper, cloth, cardboard, wood, metal, glass, leather, plastic, etc. Specially prepared water colors, oil colors, dyes, lacquers, glues, waterproof poster colors, and enamels may be used to good advantage with the screen technique.

4. FLEXIBLE SIZE

The only limit to the size of the printing area is the size of the frame used. Very large stencils may be made, and conversely, very small pieces may be printed.

FRAME CONSTRUCTION

1. Stock should be at least 1" x 1" for a 10" x 18" frame. For frames larger than this, a heavier stock should be used. Use clear white pine or Mahogany.

2. After the frame is completed, cut a ⅛" wide x ½" groove (saw cut) in under side of frame (Fig. 1).

3. Round inside edge of groove, paying special attention to the corners: this is done so the screen fabric will not tear when stretched.

4. Apply finish to the frame.

5. Mount back bar to base (Fig. 2). Use ¼" dia. x 3" stove bolts with wing nuts to make the height of the frame adjustable.

6. Attach frame to back bar (a loose pin hinge is recommended).

ATTACH SCREEN FABRIC TO FRAME

1. Cut screen fabric 3 inches larger than inside dimension of frame.
2. Cut enough ⅛″ dia. cord to encircle frame in groove.
3. Attach screen fabric to frame (be careful to apply pressure evenly; it will be necessary to go around frame 3 or 4 times).
4. Dampen screen fabric then staple to frame. Drive cord into groove with a mallet.

CUTTING FILM

1. Tape design to drawing board or table.
2. Tape stencil film over design. (Use water based stencil film.) Use only enough stencil film to cover design.
3. Select a sharp thin-bladed knife.
4. Follow the design with knife, being careful not to cut through the wax paper backing of the stencil film.

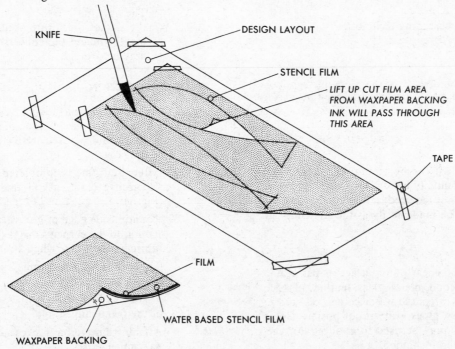

KNIFE

DESIGN LAYOUT

STENCIL FILM

LIFT UP CUT FILM AREA FROM WAXPAPER BACKING INK WILL PASS THROUGH THIS AREA

TAPE

FILM

WATER BASED STENCIL FILM

WAXPAPER BACKING

ADHERING WATER-BASED STENCIL FILM TO SCREEN

1. Position film (film side up) under screen.
2. Apply water; moisten with a small sponge by stippling with sponge—not rubbing across film.
3. Apply stippling process to one corner of the film.
4. Continue to work small areas until film is completely adhered to screen.
5. If too much water is applied or left on too long, it will burn your stencil (the film will dissolve).
6. Place a paper over damp film area with a hard desk surface behind it. Roll with pressure with a brayer. This will push the film material up into the screen.

BLOCK OUT (LARGE NONPRINTING AREAS)

1. Working on underside of screen, pour small amount of water-based block-out liquid on back of film (be sure you have not removed wax paper backing from film).
2. Use a small piece of cardboard (3 x 3) to squeegee block-out liquid over all open areas of screen.

3. Work a small area at a time; a very light coat.
4. If too much block-out liquid is used, it will seep through the screen fabric to the top side.
5. After this is completed, check the top side of screen for seepage. With cardboard squeegee, remove excess, (do not squeegee across film; this will block out the area where the ink must pass through.)

   The reason for removing excess block-out fluid from top side of screen is to keep it smooth; if it is not smooth, it will hinder your printing and wear out your squeegee.
6. After block-out liquid has dried, apply another coat of block-out, following the same procedures as above. After liquid has dried the second time, *peel wax paper backing from film.*

REGISTERING STOCK

1. Place stock or copy under screen.
2. Place guides to the bottom base and left of stock for centering purposes.

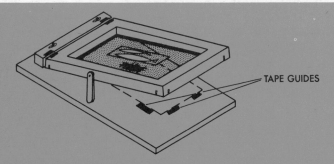

TAPE GUIDES

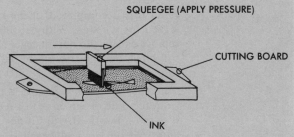

LOOSE FRAME PRINTING

SQUEEGEE (APPLY PRESSURE)

CUTTING BOARD

INK

ENCLOSE RESERVOIR AREA

1. Tape inside of frame; this will prevent ink from building up between the screen fabric and the bottom of the frame.
2. You are now ready to print.

CLEANING THE SCREEN

1. Place several layers of newspaper under screen.
2. Clean with a solvent (turpentine for enamel inks).

REMOVING STENCIL

1. Use warm water and a sponge.

BIBLIOGRAPHY

Eisenberg, James, and Kafka, Francis J., *Silk Screen Printing.* Bloomington, Illinois: McKnight & McKnight Publishing Company, 1957.

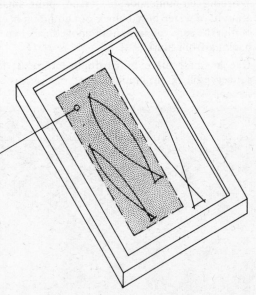

COVERING CUT STENCIL AREAS WITH A PAPER GIVES VERSATILITY IN POSITIONING SHAPES ON A SURFACE

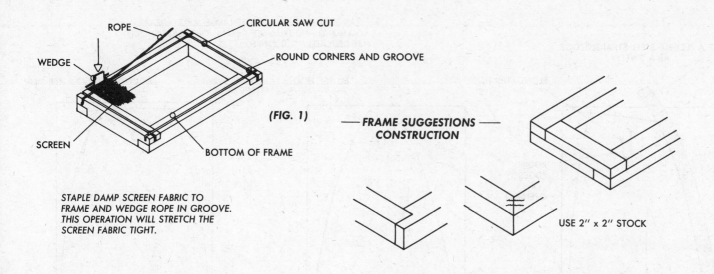

ROPE

CIRCULAR SAW CUT

WEDGE

ROUND CORNERS AND GROOVE

SCREEN

BOTTOM OF FRAME

(FIG. 1)

STAPLE DAMP SCREEN FABRIC TO
FRAME AND WEDGE ROPE IN GROOVE.
THIS OPERATION WILL STRETCH THE
SCREEN FABRIC TIGHT.

— FRAME SUGGESTIONS —
CONSTRUCTION

USE 2″ x 2″ STOCK

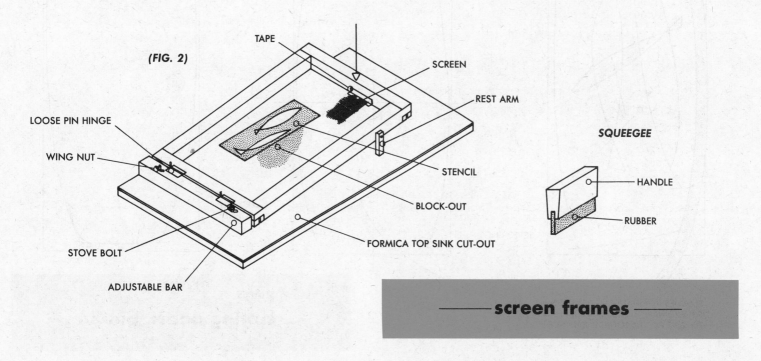

(FIG. 2)

TAPE

SCREEN

REST ARM

LOOSE PIN HINGE

WING NUT

STENCIL

BLOCK-OUT

FORMICA TOP SINK CUT-OUT

STOVE BOLT

ADJUSTABLE BAR

SQUEEGEE

HANDLE

RUBBER

screen frames

139

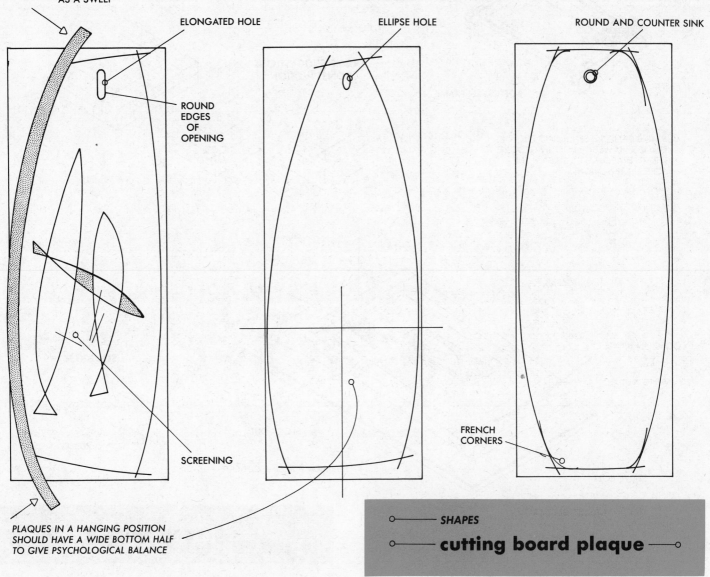

HANGER OPENINGS MUST BE LARGE; AVOID HEART, DIAMOND AND TRIANGLE SHAPES; OPENINGS SHOULD BE DELICATELY SCULPTURED.

USE A FLEXIBLE STEEL STRAIGHTEDGE AS A SWEEP

ELONGATED HOLE

ELLIPSE HOLE

ROUND AND COUNTER SINK

ROUND EDGES OF OPENING

SCREENING

FRENCH CORNERS

PLAQUES IN A HANGING POSITION SHOULD HAVE A WIDE BOTTOM HALF TO GIVE PSYCHOLOGICAL BALANCE

SHAPES

cutting board plaque

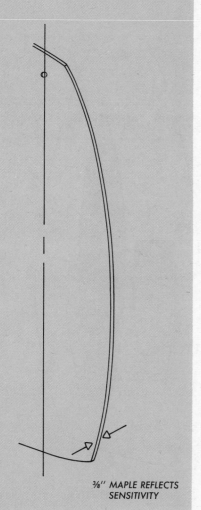

3⁄8" MAPLE REFLECTS SENSITIVITY

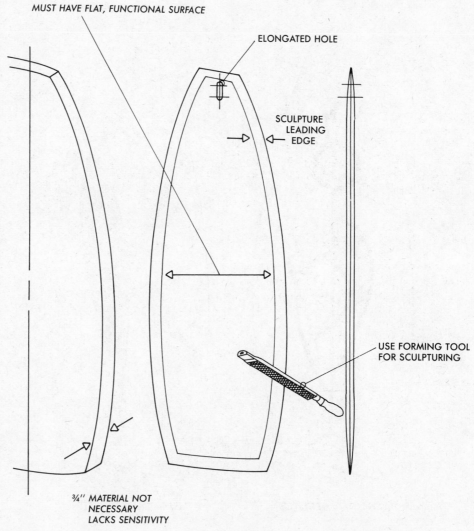

MUST HAVE FLAT, FUNCTIONAL SURFACE

ELONGATED HOLE

SCULPTURE LEADING EDGE

USE FORMING TOOL FOR SCULPTURING

3⁄4" MATERIAL NOT NECESSARY LACKS SENSITIVITY

•━━ **cutting board plaque** ━━•

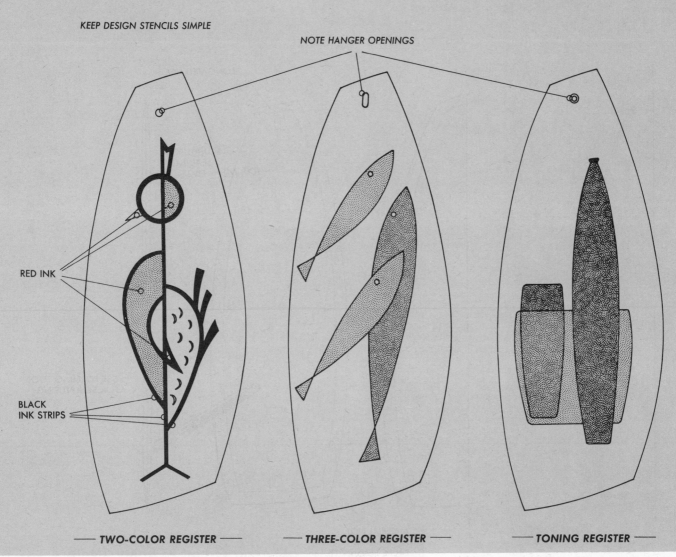

KEEP DESIGN STENCILS SIMPLE

NOTE HANGER OPENINGS

RED INK

BLACK
INK STRIPS

— TWO-COLOR REGISTER —   — THREE-COLOR REGISTER —   — TONING REGISTER —

● —— **many colors**

● —— **screening designs**

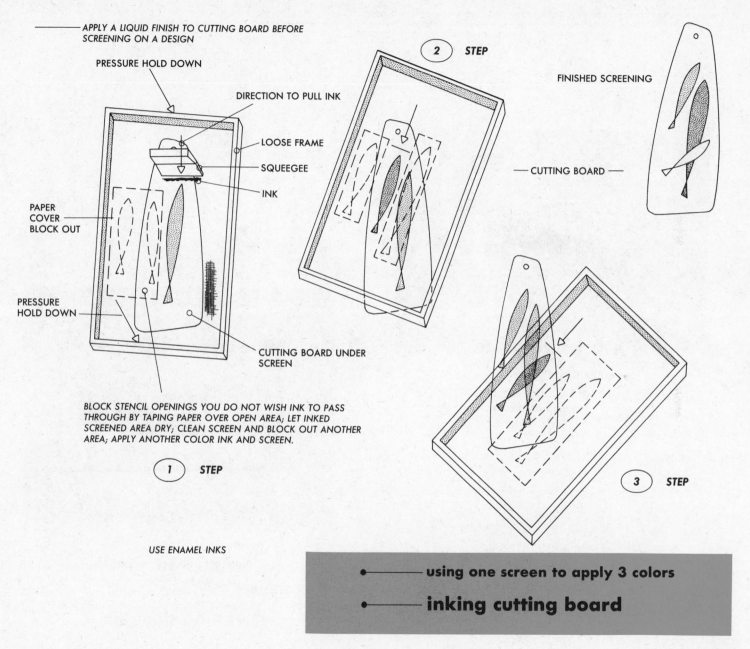

APPLY A LIQUID FINISH TO CUTTING BOARD BEFORE
SCREENING ON A DESIGN

PRESSURE HOLD DOWN

DIRECTION TO PULL INK

LOOSE FRAME

SQUEEGEE

INK

PAPER
COVER
BLOCK OUT

PRESSURE
HOLD DOWN

CUTTING BOARD UNDER
SCREEN

BLOCK STENCIL OPENINGS YOU DO NOT WISH INK TO PASS
THROUGH BY TAPING PAPER OVER OPEN AREA; LET INKED
SCREENED AREA DRY; CLEAN SCREEN AND BLOCK OUT ANOTHER
AREA; APPLY ANOTHER COLOR INK AND SCREEN.

1 STEP

USE ENAMEL INKS

2 STEP

FINISHED SCREENING

CUTTING BOARD

3 STEP

using one screen to apply 3 colors

inking cutting board

143

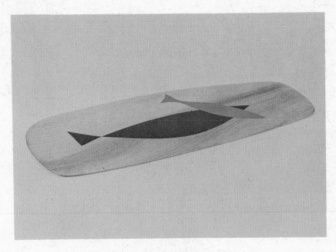

Cutting Board
Note: Screening shapes
Sculptured edges

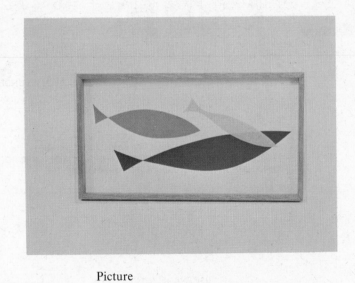

Picture
Note: Matt board background
Wood frame

144

CHAPTER **9**

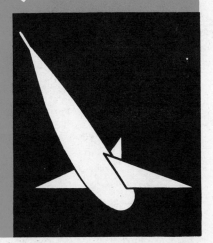

DRAFTING AND TRANSPORTATION

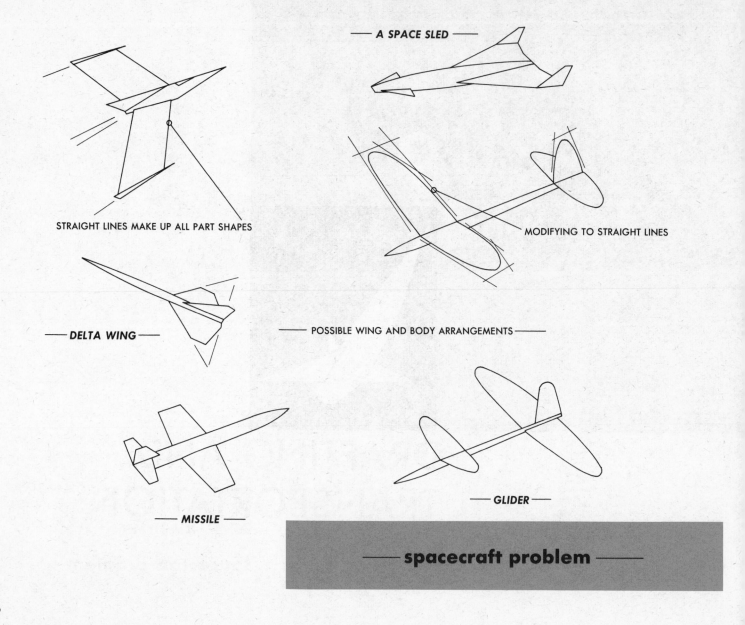

— A SPACE SLED —

STRAIGHT LINES MAKE UP ALL PART SHAPES

MODIFYING TO STRAIGHT LINES

— DELTA WING —

— POSSIBLE WING AND BODY ARRANGEMENTS —

— GLIDER —

— MISSILE —

— **spacecraft problem** —

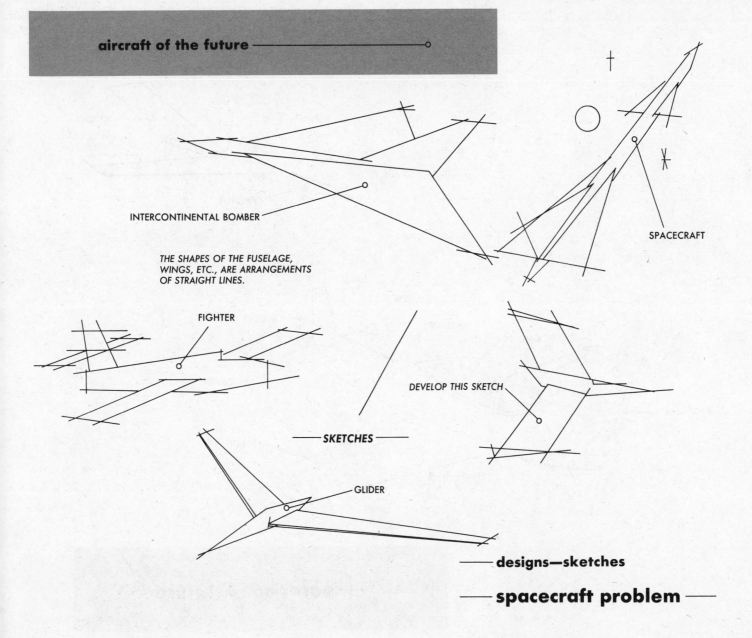

aircraft of the future

INTERCONTINENTAL BOMBER

SPACECRAFT

THE SHAPES OF THE FUSELAGE, WINGS, ETC., ARE ARRANGEMENTS OF STRAIGHT LINES.

FIGHTER

DEVELOP THIS SKETCH

SKETCHES

GLIDER

designs—sketches

spacecraft problem

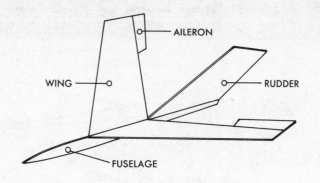

AILERON

WING

RUDDER

FUSELAGE

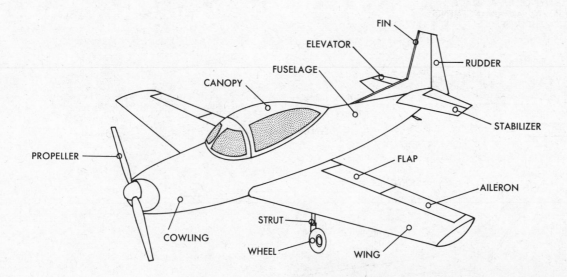

FIN

ELEVATOR

FUSELAGE

CANOPY

RUDDER

STABILIZER

PROPELLER

FLAP

AILERON

STRUT

COWLING

WHEEL

WING

—aircraft nomenclature—

problem: DESIGN AN AIRCRAFT, MISSILE OR SPACECRAFT OF TOMORROW

TOTAL PROBLEM:

1. Sketches
2. Multiview drawing (front and top view—grid drawing)
3. Isometric drawing
4. Rendering of the isometric drawing
5. Model (full scale and use balsa wood)
6. Package

LIMITATIONS OF PROBLEM:

The shapes of the fuselage, wings, etc., should be arrangements of straight lines.

SUGGESTED MATERIALS:

12″ x 17″ Tracing paper
12″ x 17″ Rendering paper
⅛″ x 3″ x 30″ Balsa wood
1⁄16″ x 3″ x 30″ Balsa wood
Colored 4-ply poster board

PHYSICAL CONSIDERATIONS:

Materials limitation (balsa wood)
Size
The model need not fly
Finish

MATERIALS:

Tracing paper
Rendering paper
Poster board
Instant lettering
⅛″ Balsa wood
1⁄16″ Balsa wood

DESIGN CONSIDERATIONS:

Envision the aircraft of tomorrow
Fuselage, wing and tail arrangement
An effective package design

MATERIAL RESOURCE:

Design Material
C-360 Design-A-Plane, 12″ to 14″ models
Actually build over 4,000 different models that you can design as well as build. Easy to take apart and create your own experimental design

Pyro Plastics Corporation
Pyro Park, Union, New Jersey

Graphics Material
Instant Lettering, poster board, etc.

Lewis Artist Supply Company
6408 Woodward Ave., Detroit 2, Michigan

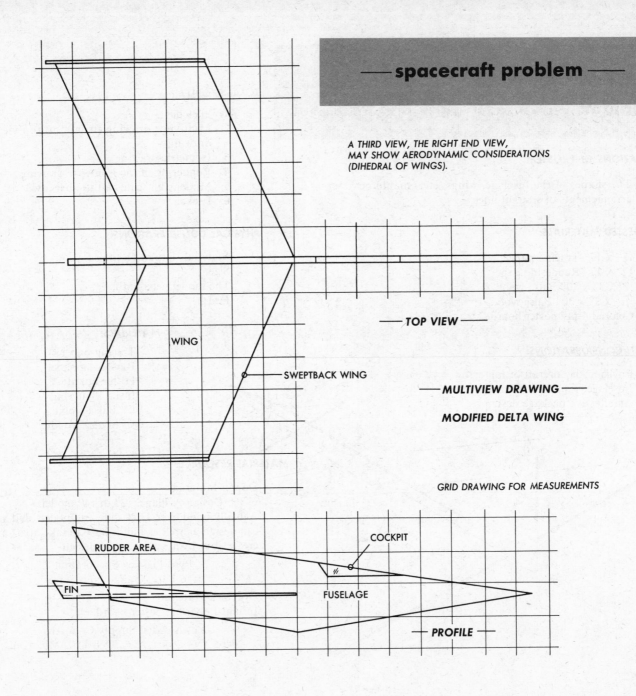

spacecraft problem

A THIRD VIEW, THE RIGHT END VIEW,
MAY SHOW AERODYNAMIC CONSIDERATIONS
(DIHEDRAL OF WINGS).

WING

SWEPTBACK WING

— TOP VIEW —

— MULTIVIEW DRAWING —

MODIFIED DELTA WING

GRID DRAWING FOR MEASUREMENTS

RUDDER AREA

COCKPIT

FIN

FUSELAGE

— PROFILE —

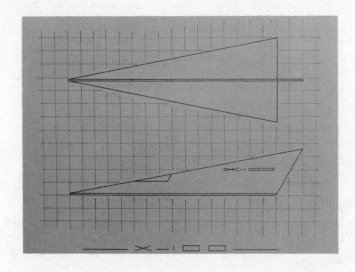

Multiview Drawing— Space Sled

Note: Two views
Grid background
The shapes of the fuselage and wings are
arrangements of straight lines

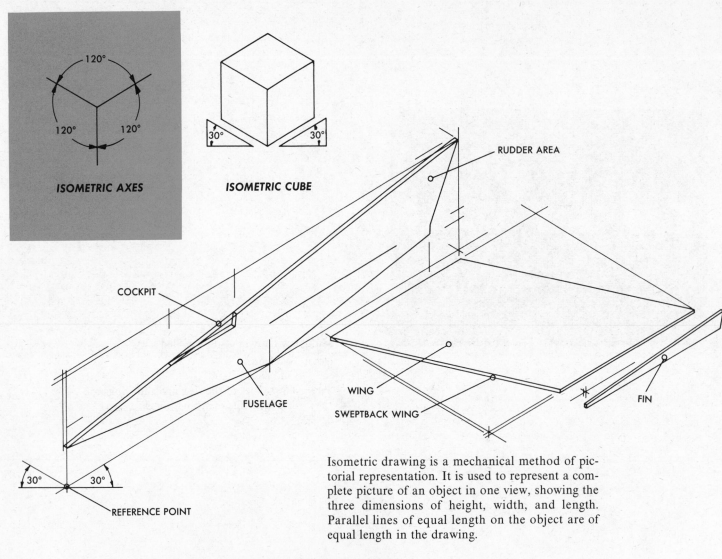

ISOMETRIC AXES

120°

120° 120°

ISOMETRIC CUBE

30° 30°

RUDDER AREA

COCKPIT

FUSELAGE

WING

SWEPTBACK WING

FIN

30° 30°

REFERENCE POINT

Isometric drawing is a mechanical method of pictorial representation. It is used to represent a complete picture of an object in one view, showing the three dimensions of height, width, and length. Parallel lines of equal length on the object are of equal length in the drawing.

—— details for isometric drawing ——

—— spacecraft problem ——

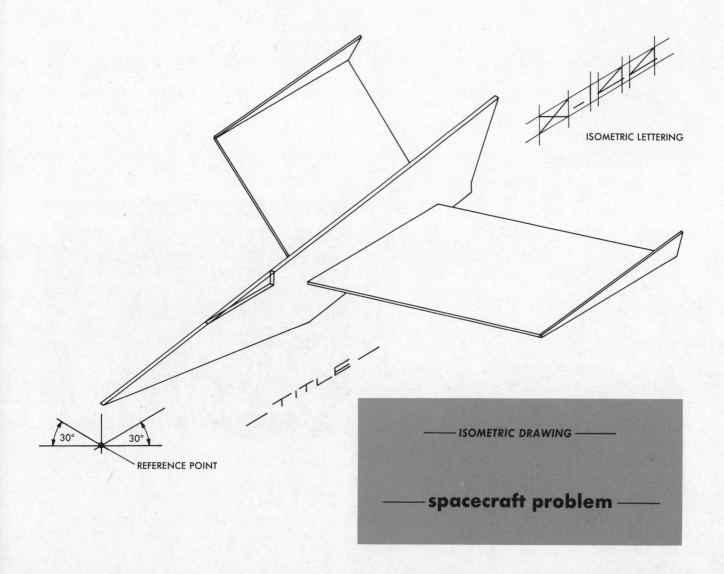

ISOMETRIC LETTERING

30° 30°
REFERENCE POINT

— TITLE —

— ISOMETRIC DRAWING —

— spacecraft problem —

153

Isometric Drawing
Note: Horizon line background
        Motion lines

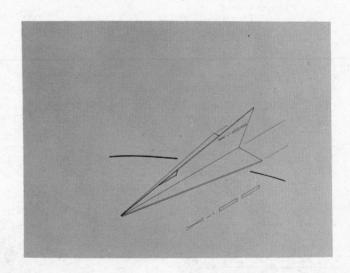

To transfer an isometric drawing to the illustration paper surface, turn the drawing upside down and trace with an "H" pencil. Then position the drawing right side up over the rendering paper and rub the lines making up the shape. The graphite on the under side of the drawing will register on the illustration paper.

DESIGN NOTE: USE ONE COLOR—DARK AND LIGHT

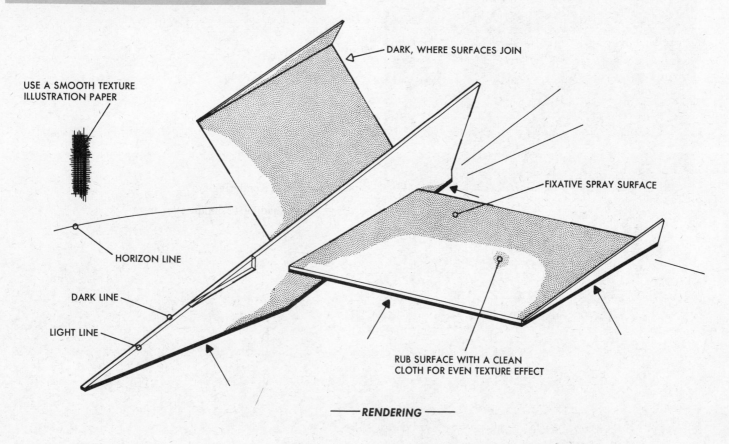

DARK, WHERE SURFACES JOIN

USE A SMOOTH TEXTURE
ILLUSTRATION PAPER

FIXATIVE SPRAY SURFACE

HORIZON LINE

DARK LINE

LIGHT LINE

RUB SURFACE WITH A CLEAN
CLOTH FOR EVEN TEXTURE EFFECT

——— RENDERING ———

——— **spacecraft problem** ———

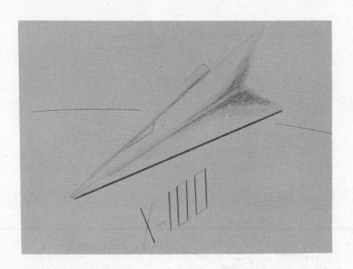

Isometric Rendering

Note: Shading Techniques

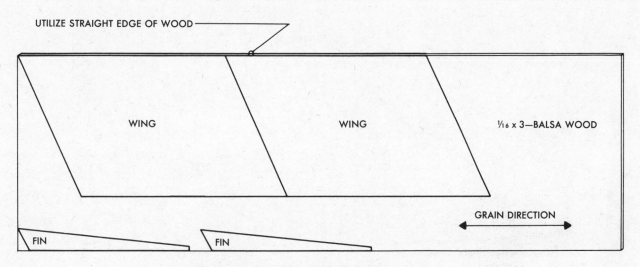

UTILIZE STRAIGHT EDGE OF WOOD

WING

WING

¹⁄₁₆ x 3—BALSA WOOD

GRAIN DIRECTION

FIN

FIN

REFER TO YOUR MULTIVIEW DRAWING FOR MEASUREMENTS

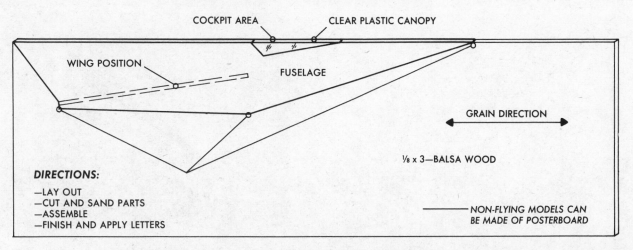

COCKPIT AREA

CLEAR PLASTIC CANOPY

WING POSITION

FUSELAGE

GRAIN DIRECTION

¹⁄₈ x 3—BALSA WOOD

DIRECTIONS:
—LAY OUT
—CUT AND SAND PARTS
—ASSEMBLE
—FINISH AND APPLY LETTERS

*NON-FLYING MODELS CAN
BE MADE OF POSTERBOARD*

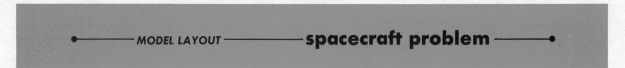

MODEL LAYOUT — **spacecraft problem**

Model
Note: Poster Board Construction
Graphics

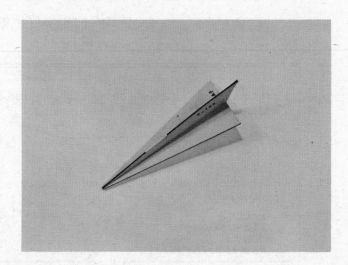

EFFECTIVE PACKAGE DESIGN CONSIDERATIONS:

1. ALLOW MAXIMUM VISUAL INSPECTION WITH MINIMUM BREAKAGE
2. ORIGINALITY
3. FUNCTION
4. SURFACE TREATMENT AND GRAPHICS

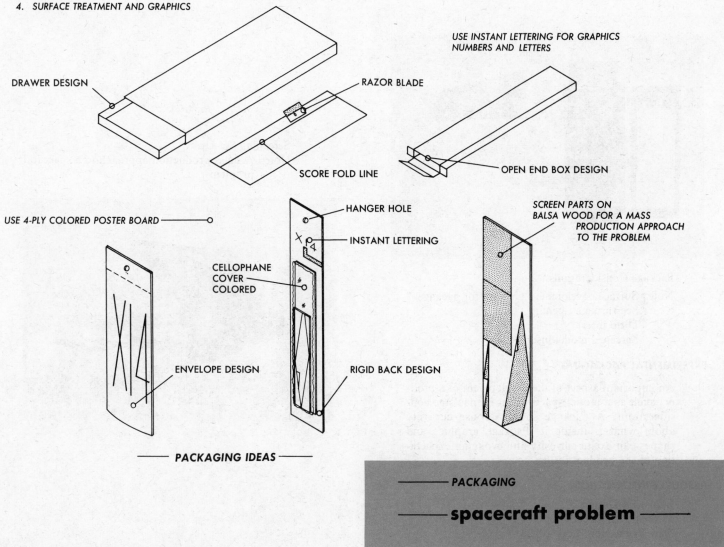

DRAWER DESIGN

RAZOR BLADE

SCORE FOLD LINE

USE INSTANT LETTERING FOR GRAPHICS NUMBERS AND LETTERS

OPEN END BOX DESIGN

USE 4-PLY COLORED POSTER BOARD

HANGER HOLE

INSTANT LETTERING

SCREEN PARTS ON BALSA WOOD FOR A MASS PRODUCTION APPROACH TO THE PROBLEM

CELLOPHANE COVER COLORED

ENVELOPE DESIGN

RIGID BACK DESIGN

PACKAGING IDEAS

PACKAGING

spacecraft problem

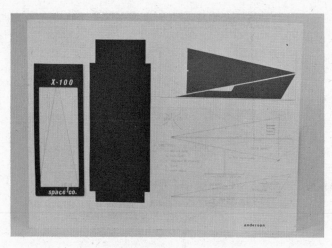

Package Considerations

Note: Surface development problem for package
See-through opening
Ditto insert
Screened model insert

EXPERIMENTAL PACKAGING

An important aspect of the development of a product such as a model spacecraft is its package considerations. A package should arouse curiosity about what is inside it. Package graphics and shapes can excite curiosity and evoke an expectation of the product inside.

RESOURCE INFORMATION:

Industrial Design
18 East 50th Street
New York, New York 10022

Screening Set-Up
Note: A mass production approach to a spacecraft problem

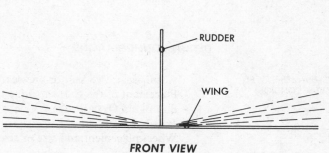

RUDDER

WING

FRONT VIEW

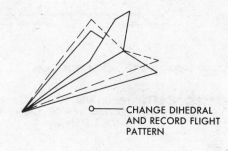

CHANGE DIHEDRAL
AND RECORD FLIGHT
PATTERN

DEGREE CHANGE

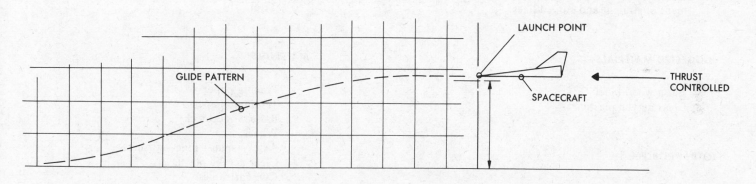

GLIDE PATTERN

LAUNCH POINT

SPACECRAFT

THRUST
CONTROLLED

BUILD A WIND TUNNEL *FOR ACCURATE
EXPERIMENTATION*

RECORD
—FLIGHT GLIDE PATTERN GRAPH
—LENGTH OF FLIGHT
—DIHEDRAL CHANGE

relationship between dihedral and glide

experimentation

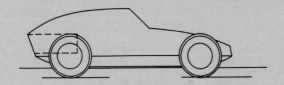

core problem: MODEL SPORTS CAR

problem: DESIGN AND CONSTRUCT A MODEL SPORTS CAR WHICH CAN BE POWERED BY A CO₂ CARTRIDGE AND WILL HAVE A CONTROL GUIDE SYSTEM

LIMITATIONS OF THE PROBLEM:

The body of the sports car should be an arrangement of straight and curved lines.

SUGGESTED MATERIALS:

Balsa wood block
Clear acrylic plastic

TOTAL PROBLEM:

1. Sketches
2. Multiview drawing (side, top, front, and end views)
3. Side and top profile templates
4. Model

PHYSICAL CONSIDERATIONS:

Material limitations (balsa wood)
Size
CO_2 cartridge power
Finish

DESIGN CONSIDERATIONS:

A four-seat, two-seat or one-seat sports car
Placement of the CO_2 cartridge
Size of a CO_2 cartridge
Possible profile forms
Wheel placement and size or sizes
Size of car
Finish
Control system
Trim

MATERIALS:

Tracing paper
Template paper
Balsa wood block
Wheels
Axles—spacer pipe—washers
Clear acrylic plastic
CO_2 cartridges
Finish materials
Lettering

MATERIAL RESOURCES: Balsa wood

Frank Paxton Lumber Company
5701 West 66th St.
Chicago 38, Illinois

Hobby supplies
A local hobby store

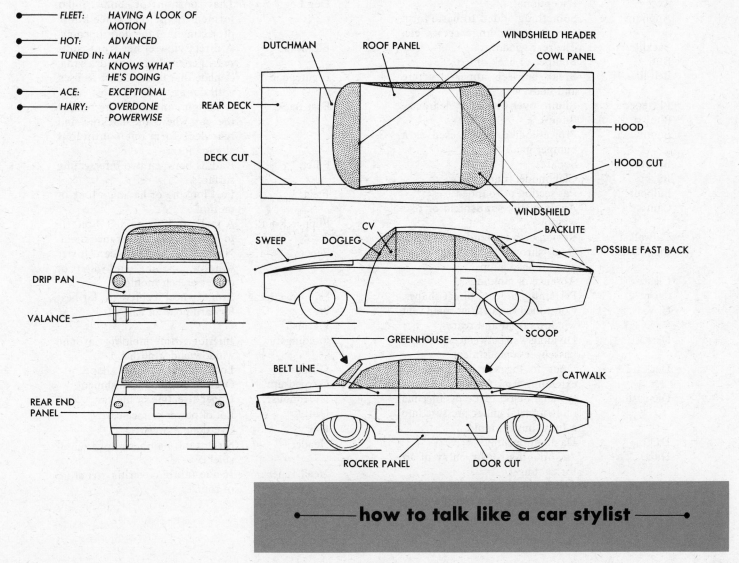

FLEET: HAVING A LOOK OF MOTION
HOT: ADVANCED
TUNED IN: MAN KNOWS WHAT HE'S DOING
ACE: EXCEPTIONAL
HAIRY: OVERDONE POWERWISE

DUTCHMAN
ROOF PANEL
WINDSHIELD HEADER
COWL PANEL
REAR DECK
HOOD
DECK CUT
HOOD CUT
WINDSHIELD

SWEEP
CV
DOGLEG
BACKLITE
POSSIBLE FAST BACK
DRIP PAN
VALANCE
SCOOP

GREENHOUSE
BELT LINE
CATWALK
REAR END PANEL
ROCKER PANEL
DOOR CUT

how to talk like a car stylist

automotive styling nomenclature

Ace:	Exceptional.
Applique:	Something added to basic form —chrome moldings, crests, etc.
Backlite:	The rear window.
BBC:	Bumper to back of cab.
Belt line:	Break between upper structure and body.
Blisters:	Bumps over wheel for clearance.
Blurps:	Bumps.
Bomb:	Projectile-like object used as a bumper guard.
Boxey:	Square.
Buck:	Clay model frame work.
Bulbous:	Fat section or rounded.
Cant:	Angle of the windshield or rear window.
Catwalks:	Region between fender and hood.
Clam Shell:	Oval shroud formed in metal around head lamps.
Clean:	Absence of moldings.
Crisp:	Pertaining to lean, direct shapes.
C. V.:	Controlled ventilation; small vent windows front and rear.
Dash:	Dividing wall between engine and passenger compartment.
Deck lid:	Door to luggage compartment extending back from backlite.
Die-casting:	A metal object made by injecting molten metal under pressure into a fully finished mold.
DLO:	Daylight opening.
Duct:	An opening to the entry of air for cooling.
Dutchman:	The metal panel that runs across the rear deck between the back-lite and deck lid.

Dog Leg:	That portion of body pillar formed by the rear wheelhouse projecting into the door opening.
Elevation:	A direct view either front, side, rear, generally in line drawing.
Escutcheon:	A plate that forms a base as used with door handles, knobs, etc.
Fast Back:	A design contour at the rear of the car where the backlite and rear deck form one continuous sloping form.
Fillet:	Radius between two intersecting surfaces.
Fleet:	Fast looking or having a look of motion.
Flipper Roof:	A method of using metal panels to provide greater entrance room.
Fence:	Narrow panel between lower window opening and fillet of fender or belt molding.
Front overhang:	Front wheel center to farthest forward point of car.
Garnish moldings:	Interior trim molding around window and windshield.
Gorpy:	Looks funny or out of shape.
Gorped-up:	Overdone with embellishment.
Greenhouse:	Upper structure of the car.
Gutty:	Lot of power or race-carrish.
Hairy:	Overdone powerwise.
Header:	Structural member above windshield.
Head Liner:	Inside fabric covering structure of roof.

Highlight:	Theoretically a path of light described by the intersection of a curved surface and a line or plane becoming tangent to that surface at a constant given angle, usually 45°.
Hot:	Advanced.
Ivory Towers:	Studios.
Jazzy:	Flashy.
Jounce:	Clearance for wheel up and down movement.
Louver:	An opening to expel heat on exhaust from engine compartment, usually on side of hood.
Low Light:	Secondary light ground reflection into body, etc.
Motif:	Main theme of a design or creative arrangement.
Notch Back:	Profile line of roof as seen from the side which breaks below back light to form deck or trunk.
O.G.:	A reverse (S) curve (ogee).
Pillar:	The narrow metal structures between windows and windshield which connect the upper structure with the lower body.
Plan View:	A line drawing viewed from the top.
Plateau:	A surface which extends above the normal sheet metal surface.
Poise:	Perfect proportion, integrated shapes and balanced line.
Pork chop:	Forward bottom half of front door cut.
Put more steam into it:	Emphasize.
Read a line:	Sight a line.
Rear overhang:	Rear wheel center to farthest rearward point of a car.
Reefer:	Refrigerated truck.
Rendering:	An illustration.

Reveal molding:	Exterior trim molding around windows and windshield.
Road clearance:	Distance from road to lowest point on the chassis.
Rolling Radius:	Diameter of tire under weight of car.
Sassy:	Appearance of high performance.
Scoop:	Unobstructed air openings for cooling radiator.
Scuff Plate:	Covering of door sill, rubber or metal.
Section:	Outline formed by cutting through a mass or object and viewing at right angles to the cut.
Serration:	A rough pattern to assist grip as sometimes used on control knobs.
Sings:	Glitters.
Spaghetti:	Overdone moldings or a number of moldings.
Spook:	Exciting—Different.
Static:	Pertaining to bodies at rest or forces in equilibrium; lack of indicated motion in style treatment.
Stacks:	Exhaust pipes.
Sweep:	A gradual curve or section of an arc.
Sweeten the line:	Correct a fault or a bad line.
Taut:	Sprightly.
Thrust:	Feeling of direction.
Tire OD:	Outside diameter of tire.
Transfer:	A pattern applied to interior trims commonly used on instrument panels.
Trim Buck:	Mock-up of car interior.
Tumble home:	The portion of body surface above the widest part of the body that sweeps up and to the center line of the body.
Tuned in:	Man knows what he is doing.
Tunnel:	The hop-up in the center of the passenger compartment that houses the drive shaft.

Turnunder:	The lower section of the body and sill.
Upper Structure:	That portion of body that contains windows and roof.
Valley:	A surface that is below two higher surfaces.
Warped surface:	Not in good condition.
Windcord:	A fabric corded seal around inside of door attached to body.
Windsplit:	A sharp narrow section emerging from a flat surface.

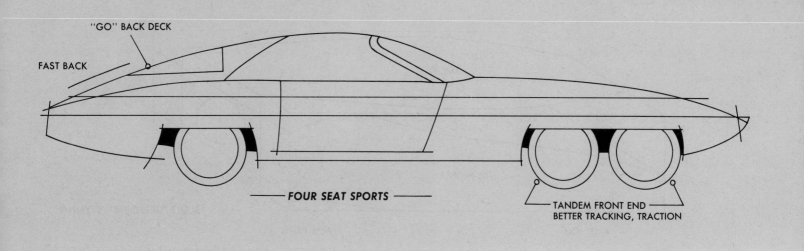

"GO" BACK DECK

FAST BACK

FOUR SEAT SPORTS

TANDEM FRONT END
BETTER TRACKING, TRACTION

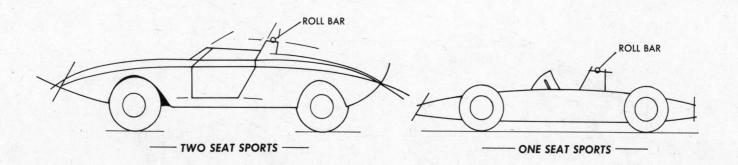

ROLL BAR

ROLL BAR

TWO SEAT SPORTS

ONE SEAT SPORTS

advanced styling ● car designs

167

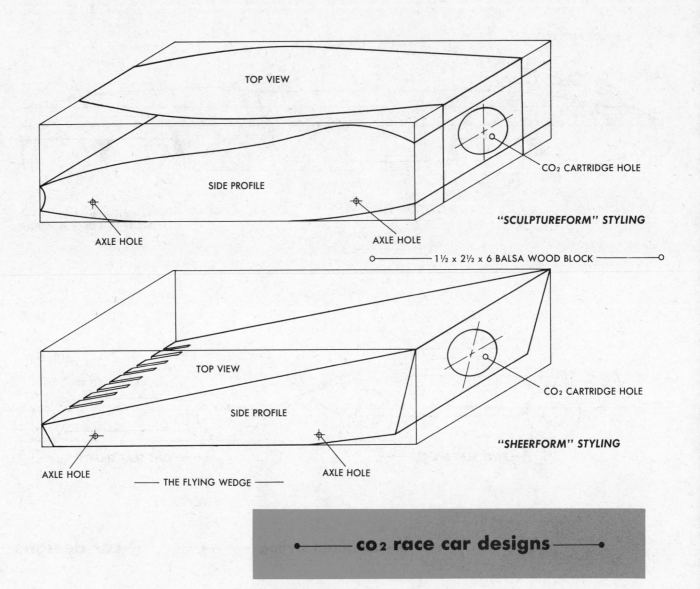

TOP VIEW

SIDE PROFILE

CO₂ CARTRIDGE HOLE

"SCULPTUREFORM" STYLING

AXLE HOLE

AXLE HOLE

1½ x 2½ x 6 BALSA WOOD BLOCK

TOP VIEW

SIDE PROFILE

CO₂ CARTRIDGE HOLE

"SHEERFORM" STYLING

AXLE HOLE

AXLE HOLE

THE FLYING WEDGE

co₂ race car designs

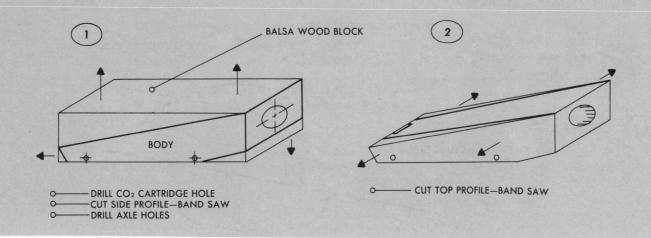

1 BALSA WOOD BLOCK

BODY

- DRILL CO$_2$ CARTRIDGE HOLE
- CUT SIDE PROFILE—BAND SAW
- DRILL AXLE HOLES

2

- CUT TOP PROFILE—BAND SAW

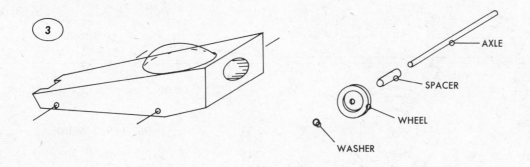

3

AXLE

SPACER

WHEEL

WASHER

- SAND
- SEAL
- PAINT
- ASSEMBLE

USE SCULPTUREFORM STYLING OR SHEERFORM STYLING

how to cut car form

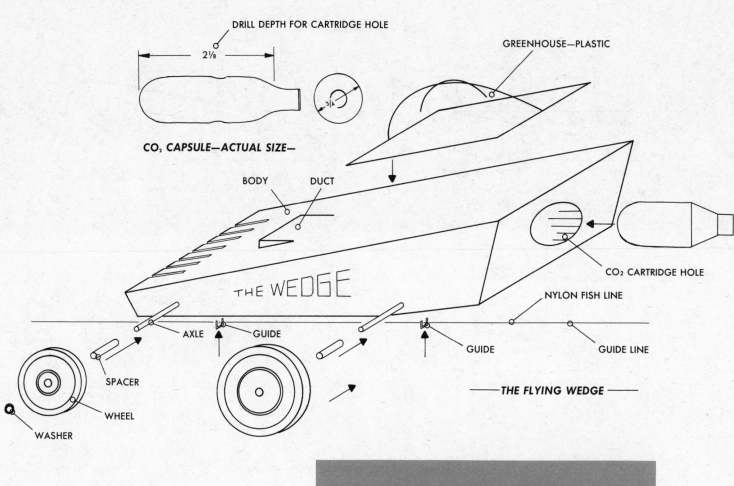

DRILL DEPTH FOR CARTRIDGE HOLE

2 1/8

CO₂ CAPSULE—ACTUAL SIZE—

3/4

GREENHOUSE—PLASTIC

BODY

DUCT

CO₂ CARTRIDGE HOLE

THE WEDGE

NYLON FISH LINE

AXLE

GUIDE

GUIDE

GUIDE LINE

SPACER

THE FLYING WEDGE

WHEEL

WASHER

co₂ race car detail

Sculptured Balsa Wood Model Race Car
Note: Design
Wheels
CO_2 cartridge·hole

● SPREAD TRI-WHEEL DESIGN CONSIDERATIONS

LIGHT WEIGHT
STABILITY
STRUCTURE
LESS MATERIAL
LIMITED BODY DESIGN
CO_2 CARTRIDGE HOLE SIZE AND POSITION
WHEEL SIZE

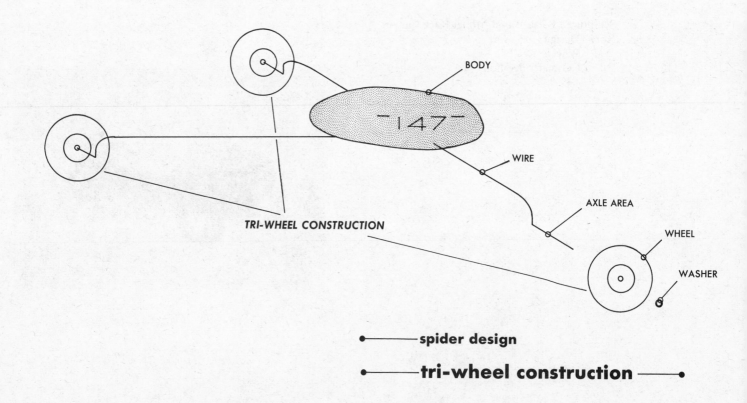

BODY

147

WIRE

AXLE AREA

WHEEL

WASHER

TRI-WHEEL CONSTRUCTION

● spider design

● **tri-wheel construction** ●

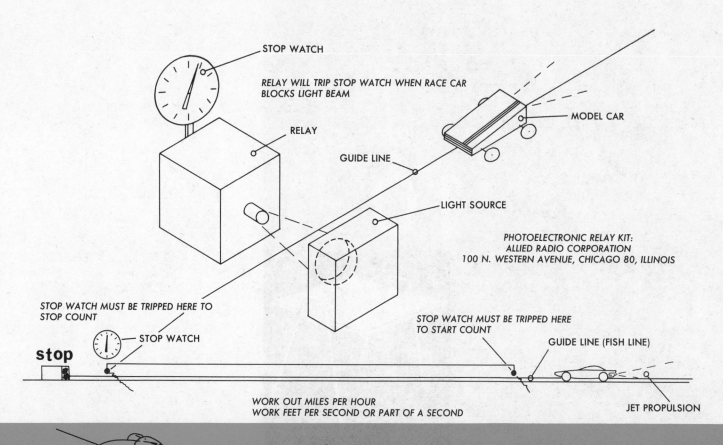

STOP WATCH

RELAY WILL TRIP STOP WATCH WHEN RACE CAR
BLOCKS LIGHT BEAM

RELAY

MODEL CAR

GUIDE LINE

LIGHT SOURCE

PHOTOELECTRONIC RELAY KIT:
ALLIED RADIO CORPORATION
100 N. WESTERN AVENUE, CHICAGO 80, ILLINOIS

STOP WATCH MUST BE TRIPPED HERE TO
STOP COUNT

STOP WATCH

stop

STOP WATCH MUST BE TRIPPED HERE
TO START COUNT

GUIDE LINE (FISH LINE)

WORK OUT MILES PER HOUR
WORK FEET PER SECOND OR PART OF A SECOND

JET PROPULSION

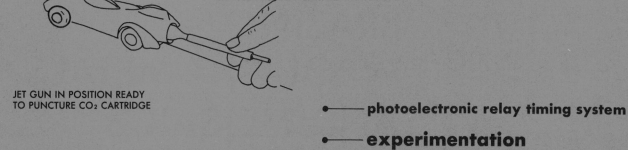

JET GUN IN POSITION READY
TO PUNCTURE CO_2 CARTRIDGE

●——— **photoelectronic relay timing system**

●——— **experimentation**

CHAPTER 10

BRAZING, WROUGHT METALS AND MOSAICS

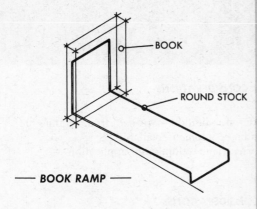

BOOK

ROUND STOCK

— BOOK RAMP —

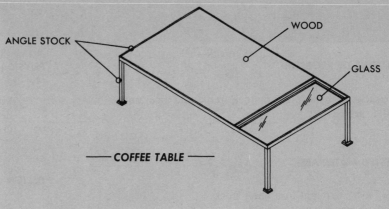

ANGLE STOCK

WOOD

GLASS

— COFFEE TABLE —

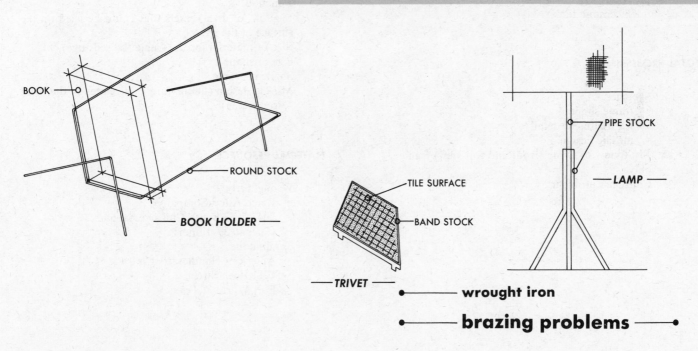

BOOK

ROUND STOCK

— BOOK HOLDER —

TILE SURFACE

BAND STOCK

— TRIVET —

PIPE STOCK

— LAMP —

wrought iron

— brazing problems —

problem: *DESIGN A WROUGHT IRON METAL TRIVET*

LIMITATIONS OF PROBLEM:

Use wrought iron band stock frame and a ceramic tile surface

SUGGESTED MATERIALS:

⅛″ x ⅜″ wrought iron band stock
¼″ plywood
⅛″ thick ceramic tile

TOTAL PROBLEM:

1. Sketches
   frame shape
   leg treatment detail
   mosaic design
2. Multiview drawing (front and top view) frame only
3. Construct problem

PHYSICAL CONSIDERATIONS:

Material limitation— wrought iron, ceramic tile
Bending equipment available
Oxyacetylene welding unit application

DESIGN CONSIDERATIONS:

Function
Size of hot dish vessels that could be used on the surface of the trivet
Size of material for the frame (be sensitive)
Size of shape
Shape of frame
Mosaic design (tile texture as it relates to the band iron frame)

MATERIAL RESOURCE:

Wrought iron
    Retco Alloy Company
    7047-7053 South Chicago Avenue
    Chicago 37, Illinois
Ceramic tile
    American Handicrafts Co.
    1011 Foch Street
    Fort Worth 7, Texas

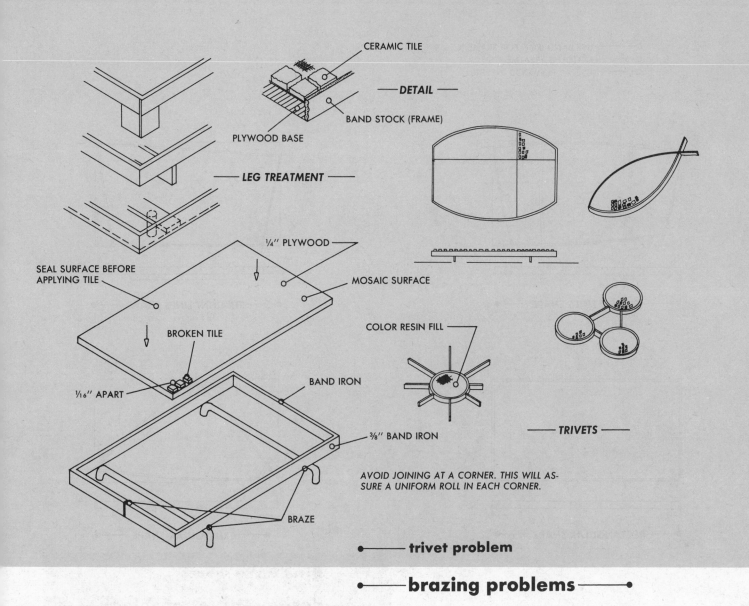

CERAMIC TILE

— *DETAIL* —

BAND STOCK (FRAME)

PLYWOOD BASE

— *LEG TREATMENT* —

¼″ PLYWOOD

SEAL SURFACE BEFORE
APPLYING TILE

MOSAIC SURFACE

BROKEN TILE

COLOR RESIN FILL

BAND IRON

¹⁄₁₆″ APART

⅜″ BAND IRON

— *TRIVETS* —

*AVOID JOINING AT A CORNER. THIS WILL AS-
SURE A UNIFORM ROLL IN EACH CORNER.*

BRAZE

trivet problem

brazing problems

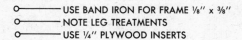

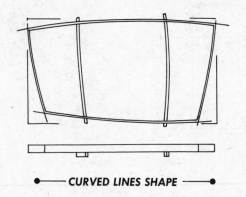

●—— **CURVED LINES SHAPE** ——●

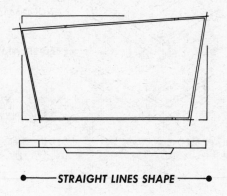

●—— **STRAIGHT LINES SHAPE** ——●

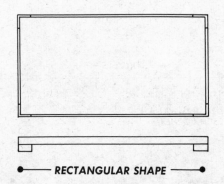

●—— **RECTANGULAR SHAPE** ——●

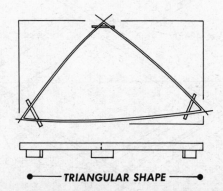

●—— **TRIANGULAR SHAPE** ——●

●—— **trivet frame shapes**

●—— **design—trivet problem** ——●

Trivet
Note: One color mosaic surface
Shapes of the broken tile
Band iron frame shape
Band iron strip legs

how to apply mosaic tile ————————————○

1. Work out a few simple designs. Choose the one design you like best; copy this design onto your problem surface. (Use plywood or masonite and seal.) Place your tile in warm water for approximately 15 minutes. (Remove paper backing.) Clean and dry thoroughly before using. (Fracture tile.)

2. Apply some white glue to a small area on the edge of your problem surface. Always work from the outside of your problem surface towards the middle.

3. Following your chosen design, start to place your tiles into the glue, making sure you space each piece of tile approximately 1⁄16″ apart. Press down on your tile firmly to assure a good bond.

4. Keep working your pattern towards the center and from time to time level the tiles with the edge of a board. *Allow tile to set 24 hours before grouting.*

5. Grouting your problem surface is very simple. Prepare the grout by adding water to the grout powder until it has a *dough consistency.* Spread the dough over a small area at a time, rubbing it into the cracks with your finger tips.

6. Remove all excess grout immediately with your finger tips; then wipe with a dry clean cloth. After 24 hours a coat of liquid *silicone grout sealer* may be applied.

MATERIAL RESOURCE:
AMERICAN HANDICRAFTS CO.
2840 WHITE SETTLEMENT RD.
FORT WORTH 7, TEXAS

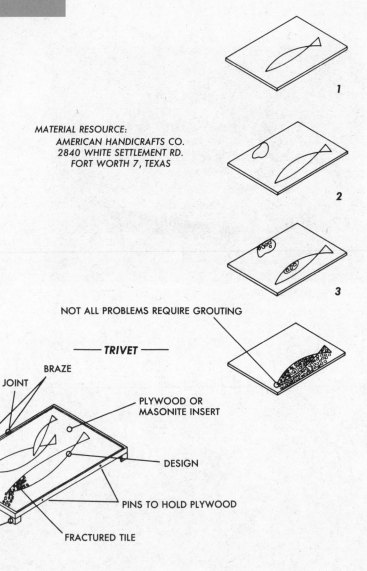

1

2

3

NOT ALL PROBLEMS REQUIRE GROUTING

———— TRIVET ————

JOINT

BRAZE

PLYWOOD OR MASONITE INSERT

DESIGN

PINS TO HOLD PLYWOOD

BAND IRON

FRACTURED TILE

ANGLE IRON LEGS

180

CUTTING THE TILES WITH TILE NIPPER

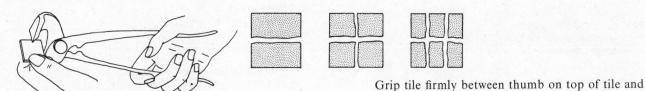

Grip tile firmly between thumb on top of tile and first two fingers on bottom so as to have hold of both pieces when cut. Place tile (just barely) in the nipper about ⅛ of an inch from the edge of the tile, lining the cutting surface up with direction that you wish the tile to break. Give the nippers a *quick squeeze* from the very end of the handle.

FILLING IN AN AREA WITH PIECES ALL CUT ON THE SQUARE

VARIOUS SHAPES AND SIZES MIXED

DIFFERENT SHADES OF THE SAME COLOR

TEXTURES... TEXTURES IN MOSAIC ARE CREATED BY:
A. COLOR AND NATURAL TEXTURE OF THE TILES.
B. SIZE AND SHAPE OF THE TILES USED.
C. DIRECTION AND PLACEMENT OF THE TILES.
D. SPACE LEFT BETWEEN THE TILES.
E. COMBINATIONS OF COLORS, ETC.
THERE ARE UNLIMITED POSSIBILITIES OF TEXTURES.

EXTRA SMALL PIECES FOR FINENESS OF DETAIL OR JUST VARIATION

A FORMAL PATTERN USING HALF-TILES

ALL TRIANGULAR PIECES FOR ANOTHER EFFECT

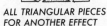

HALF-TILES USED TO FOLLOW A CURVE

WEDGE SHAPED TILES USED TO FOLLOW A CURVE

HALF-TILES USED TO FOLLOW A CURVE

WHEEL EFFECT

THREE-DIMENSIONAL TEXTURES AND EXPERIMENTATION

BY APPLICATION OF THE TILES IN AN UNORTHODOX PLACE-MENT, UNUSUAL RESULTS ARE OFTEN ACHIEVED.

PIECES STOOD ON EDGE FOR A HIGHLY TEXTURED AREA OR EMPHASIS.

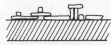

PIECES ON TOP OF PIECES FOR A "SCULPTURAL LOOK".

SLANTED PIECES OVER-LAPPING TO GIVE AN EFFECT OF SCALES OR LEAVES.

CRUSHED TILES FOR A "GRAVEL" OR "SAND" EFFECT.

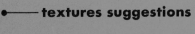

● — textures suggestions

● — **mosaic textures**

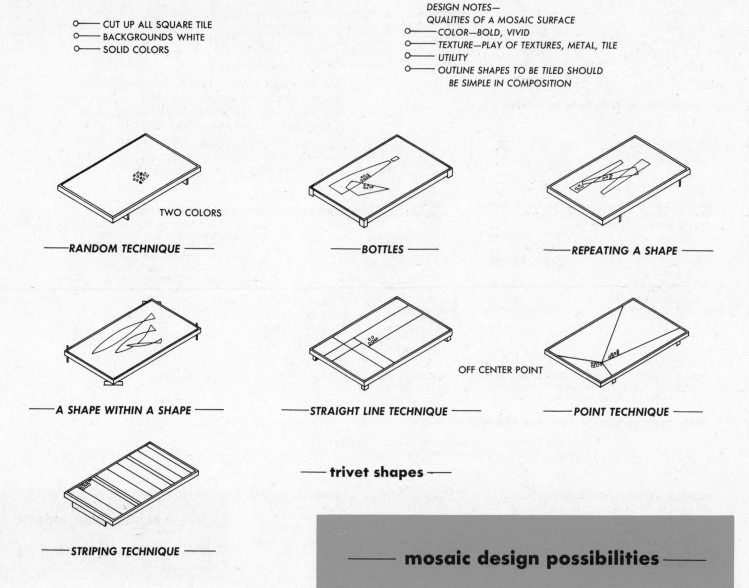

CUT UP ALL SQUARE TILE
BACKGROUNDS WHITE
SOLID COLORS

DESIGN NOTES—
QUALITIES OF A MOSAIC SURFACE
COLOR—BOLD, VIVID
TEXTURE—PLAY OF TEXTURES, METAL, TILE
UTILITY
OUTLINE SHAPES TO BE TILED SHOULD
BE SIMPLE IN COMPOSITION

TWO COLORS

— RANDOM TECHNIQUE —

— BOTTLES —

— REPEATING A SHAPE —

— A SHAPE WITHIN A SHAPE —

— STRAIGHT LINE TECHNIQUE —

OFF CENTER POINT

— POINT TECHNIQUE —

— trivet shapes —

— STRIPING TECHNIQUE —

— mosaic design possibilities —

182

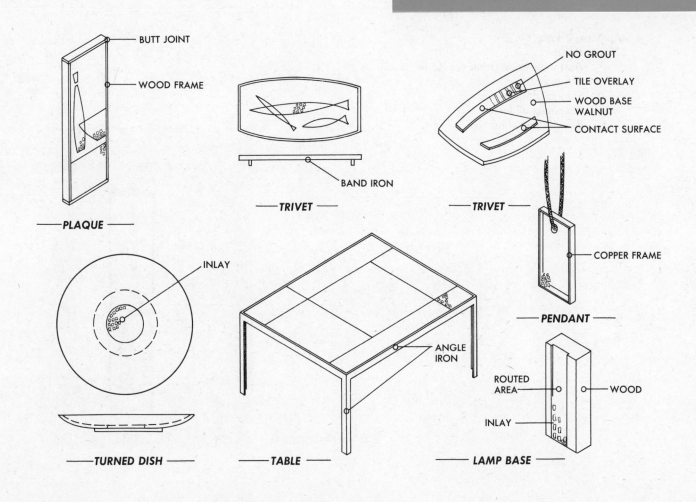

BUTT JOINT

WOOD FRAME

PLAQUE

NO GROUT

TILE OVERLAY

WOOD BASE
WALNUT

CONTACT SURFACE

TRIVET

BAND IRON

TRIVET

COPPER FRAME

PENDANT

INLAY

ANGLE
IRON

ROUTED
AREA

WOOD

INLAY

TURNED DISH

TABLE

LAMP BASE

183

Strip Mosaic Plaque
   Note: Hanger
          Butt joint wood frame (could be band iron
             frame)
          Subject for design
          Simplicity of design
          Background color

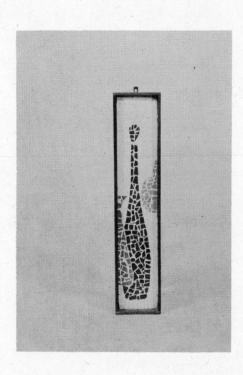

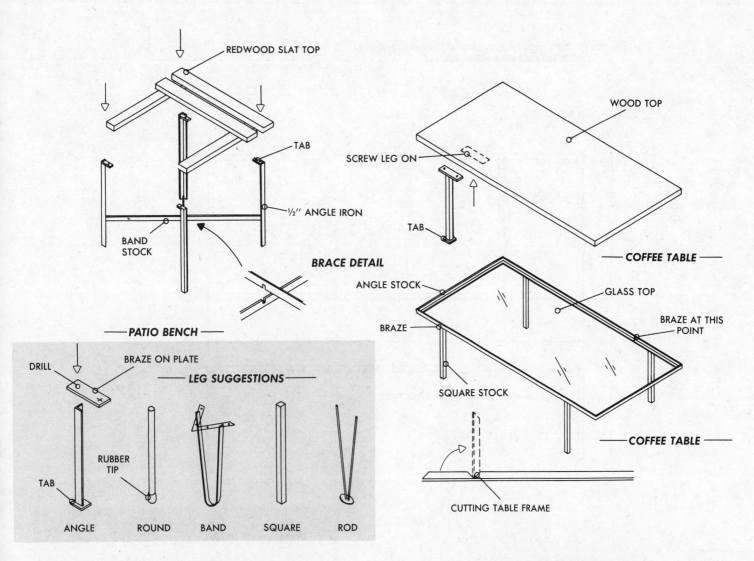

REDWOOD SLAT TOP

TAB

½" ANGLE IRON

BAND STOCK

BRACE DETAIL

— PATIO BENCH —

DRILL

BRAZE ON PLATE

— LEG SUGGESTIONS —

RUBBER TIP

TAB

ANGLE   ROUND   BAND   SQUARE   ROD

WOOD TOP

SCREW LEG ON

TAB

— COFFEE TABLE —

ANGLE STOCK

GLASS TOP

BRAZE AT THIS POINT

BRAZE

SQUARE STOCK

— COFFEE TABLE —

CUTTING TABLE FRAME

• table problems •

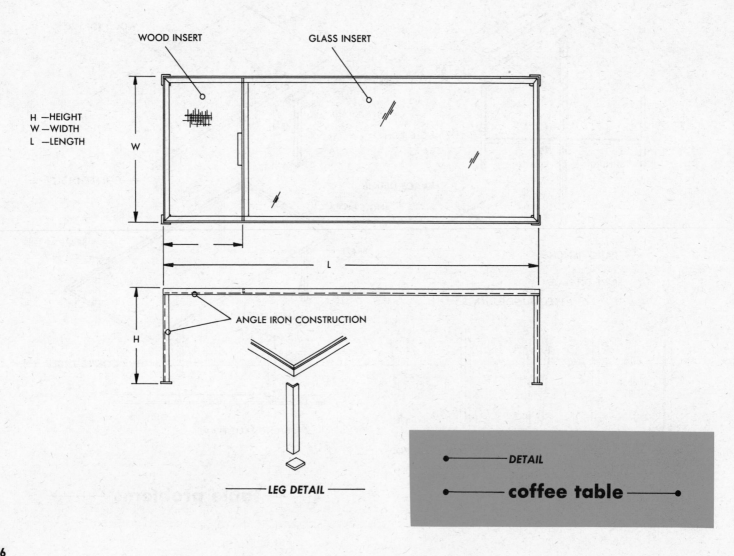

DESIGN NOTE: USEFULNESS AND PRACTICALITY ARE THE PRINCIPAL
ADVANTAGES OF A PLANE SURFACE.

WOOD INSERT

GLASS INSERT

H —HEIGHT
W —WIDTH
L —LENGTH

W

L

ANGLE IRON CONSTRUCTION

H

LEG DETAIL

DETAIL

coffee table

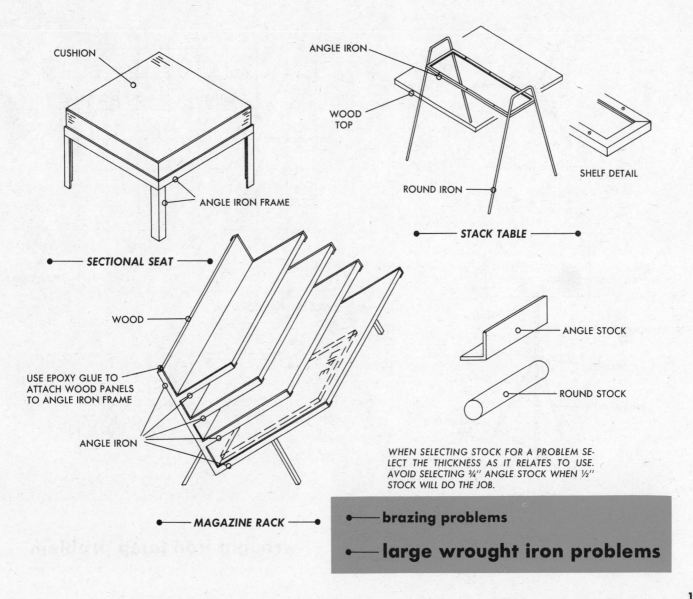

CUSHION

ANGLE IRON FRAME

SECTIONAL SEAT

ANGLE IRON

WOOD TOP

ROUND IRON

SHELF DETAIL

STACK TABLE

WOOD

USE EPOXY GLUE TO ATTACH WOOD PANELS TO ANGLE IRON FRAME

ANGLE IRON

ANGLE STOCK

ROUND STOCK

WHEN SELECTING STOCK FOR A PROBLEM SELECT THE THICKNESS AS IT RELATES TO USE. AVOID SELECTING ¾" ANGLE STOCK WHEN ½" STOCK WILL DO THE JOB.

MAGAZINE RACK

brazing problems

large wrought iron problems

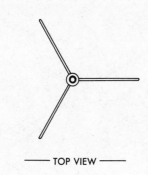

TOP VIEW

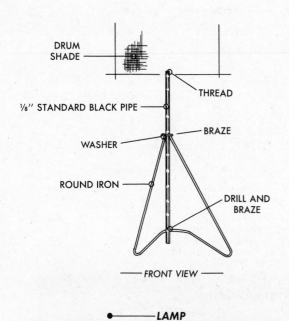

DRUM SHADE

THREAD

1/8" STANDARD BLACK PIPE

BRAZE

WASHER

ROUND IRON

DRILL AND BRAZE

FRONT VIEW

LAMP

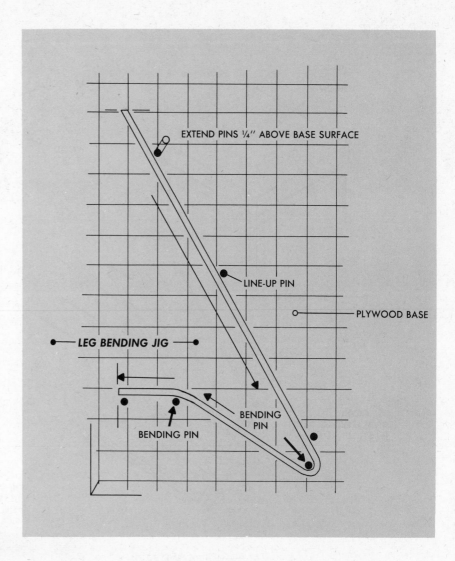

EXTEND PINS 1/4" ABOVE BASE SURFACE

LINE-UP PIN

PLYWOOD BASE

LEG BENDING JIG

BENDING PIN

BENDING PIN

BENDING PIN

wrought iron lamp problem

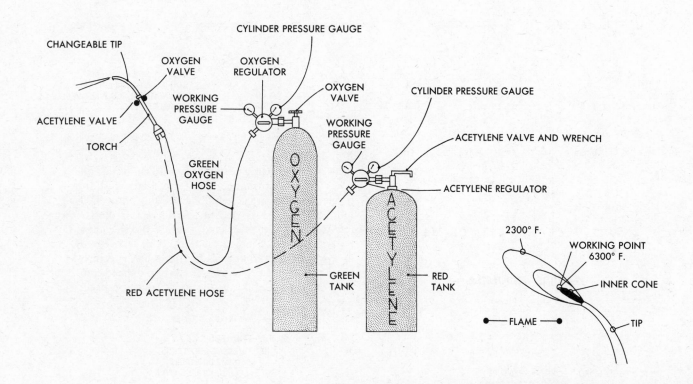

CHANGEABLE TIP

OXYGEN VALVE

CYLINDER PRESSURE GAUGE

OXYGEN REGULATOR

WORKING PRESSURE GAUGE

OXYGEN VALVE

CYLINDER PRESSURE GAUGE

ACETYLENE VALVE

WORKING PRESSURE GAUGE

ACETYLENE VALVE AND WRENCH

TORCH

ACETYLENE REGULATOR

GREEN OXYGEN HOSE

OXYGEN

ACETYLENE

RED ACETYLENE HOSE

GREEN TANK

RED TANK

2300° F.

WORKING POINT 6300° F.

INNER CONE

FLAME

TIP

NOMENCLATURE

oxyacetylene welding unit

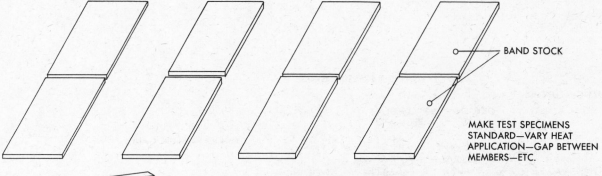

BAND STOCK

MAKE TEST SPECIMENS
STANDARD—VARY HEAT
APPLICATION—GAP BETWEEN
MEMBERS—ETC.

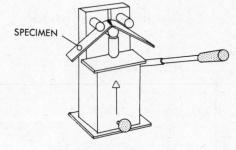

SPECIMEN

— *GUIDE BEND TESTER* —

A guided bend test is the most useful single test of welder and brazing proficiency and of weld and braze joint performance. The tester loads and deforms a weld or braze joint in a carefully controlled manner. The test is very fast and is a GO or NO GO test in that if there is no rupture the specimen passes. A fracture indicates failure. This test is used as a weld and welder qualifications test specified by the American Welding Society. Its speed and ease of reading makes it the most common of all tests.

GUIDE BEND TESTER
BRODHEAD-GARRETT CO.
4560 E. 71st STREET
CLEVELAND, OHIO 44105

● — RECORD: *RUPTURE PRESSURE*
   SPECIMEN DESCRIPTION

● —— **test weld and braze joint performance**

● —— **experimentation**

CHAPTER 11

SHEET METAL
AND WIRE SCULPTURE

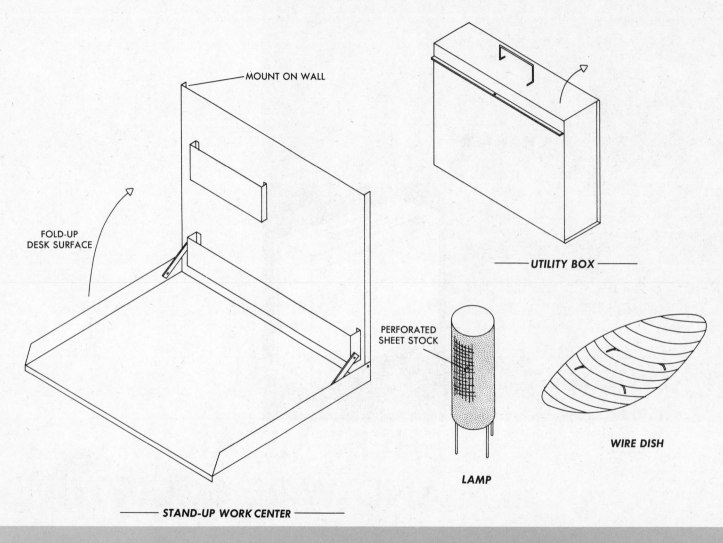

MOUNT ON WALL

FOLD-UP
DESK SURFACE

PERFORATED
SHEET STOCK

UTILITY BOX

LAMP

WIRE DISH

STAND-UP WORK CENTER

sheet metal and wire problems

LIMITATIONS OF PROBLEM:

Use cold rolled sheet steel

SUGGESTED MATERIALS:

22 Gauge ferrous cold rolled sheet steel
$\frac{3}{16}''$ Diameter cold rolled round stock or mild copper coated welding rod
Piano hinge

TOTAL PROBLEM:

1. Sketches
2. Multiview drawing, full size, three views or draw each member sheet metal blank shape.
3. Full size posterboard model with handle and clasp solutions.
4. Full size prototype.
5. Written summary
   The written summary should be a brief statement giving the main points of the problem.

PHYSICAL CONSIDERATIONS:

Materials limitation
Physical properties of cold rolled sheet
Spot welding limitations
Finish
Tools and equipment available

DESIGN CONSIDERATIONS:

Rid yourself of utility box stereotypes
What will the box hold? (function)
Only functional designs can be good designs
Finish, color
Size and cost relation
Body, ends, lid, handle relation
Handle size and shape
Clasp, type and size
Styling Sheerform

MATERIALS:

22 Gauge cold rolled sheet steel stock
$\frac{3}{16}''$ Diameter cold rolled round stock
Spray can paint
1'' Wide piano hinge

MATERIAL RESOURCE: Cold rolled sheet metal stock
Retco Alloy Company
7047-7053 South Chicago Avenue
Chicago 37, Illinois

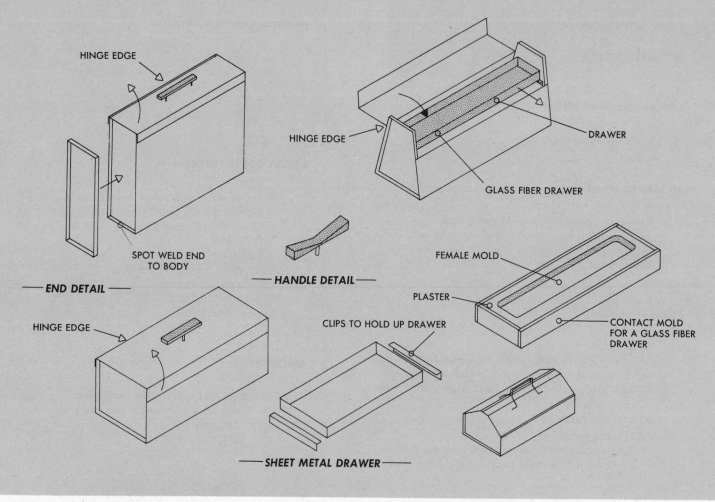

HINGE EDGE

HINGE EDGE

DRAWER

GLASS FIBER DRAWER

SPOT WELD END
TO BODY

HANDLE DETAIL

FEMALE MOLD

PLASTER

CONTACT MOLD
FOR A GLASS FIBER
DRAWER

END DETAIL

HINGE EDGE

CLIPS TO HOLD UP DRAWER

SHEET METAL DRAWER

utility boxes

sheet metal problems

194

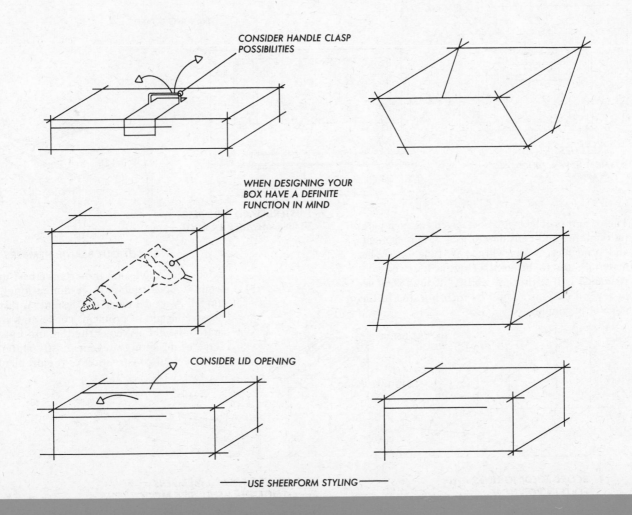

CONSIDER HANDLE CLASP
POSSIBILITIES

WHEN DESIGNING YOUR
BOX HAVE A DEFINITE
FUNCTION IN MIND

CONSIDER LID OPENING

USE SHEERFORM STYLING

design—utility box

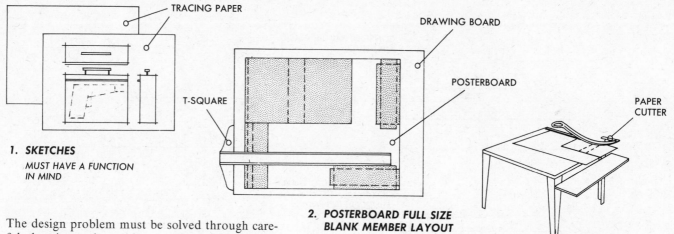

TRACING PAPER

DRAWING BOARD

POSTERBOARD

PAPER CUTTER

T-SQUARE

1. SKETCHES
MUST HAVE A FUNCTION IN MIND

2. POSTERBOARD FULL SIZE BLANK MEMBER LAYOUT

3. CUT OUT BLANK MEMBERS

The design problem must be solved through careful planning and consideration of design elements and principles. What will be its function? What materials are to be used? How is it to be constructed? Is it within my ability? Rough sketches of several designs should be incorporated in this stage of planning.

Select the sketch that imparts the best design and from it construct a three-dimensional, full-size model. A model gives the designer a fast comprehensive insight of problems concerning size, shape, materials, details, construction and finishes. This stage of designing prevents costly material errors in the actual construction of the problem.

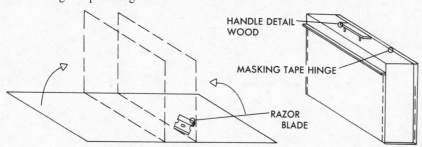

HANDLE DETAIL WOOD

MASKING TAPE HINGE

RAZOR BLADE

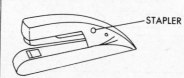

STAPLER

4. SCORE FOLDING LINES AND FOLD IN POSITION

5. STAPLE FOLDED MEMBERS TOGETHER—FULL-SIZE MODEL

●————— sheet metal planning techniques

●————**3-dimension model**

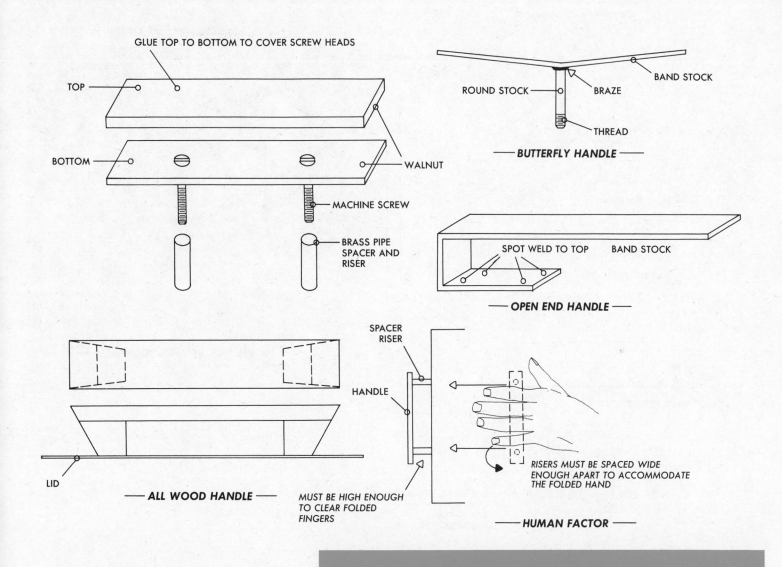

GLUE TOP TO BOTTOM TO COVER SCREW HEADS

TOP

BOTTOM

WALNUT

MACHINE SCREW

BRASS PIPE SPACER AND RISER

— BUTTERFLY HANDLE —

ROUND STOCK

BRAZE

BAND STOCK

THREAD

SPOT WELD TO TOP   BAND STOCK

— OPEN END HANDLE —

SPACER RISER

HANDLE

LID

— ALL WOOD HANDLE —

MUST BE HIGH ENOUGH TO CLEAR FOLDED FINGERS

RISERS MUST BE SPACED WIDE ENOUGH APART TO ACCOMMODATE THE FOLDED HAND

— HUMAN FACTOR —

handle design considerations

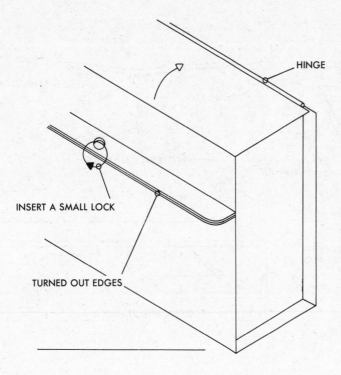

HINGE

INSERT A SMALL LOCK

TURNED OUT EDGES

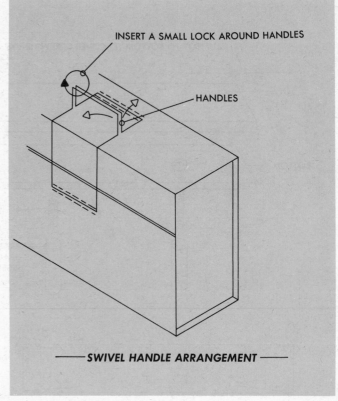

INSERT A SMALL LOCK AROUND HANDLES

HANDLES

SWIVEL HANDLE ARRANGEMENT

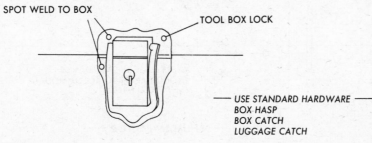

SPOT WELD TO BOX

TOOL BOX LOCK

USE STANDARD HARDWARE
BOX HASP
BOX CATCH
LUGGAGE CATCH

lock considerations

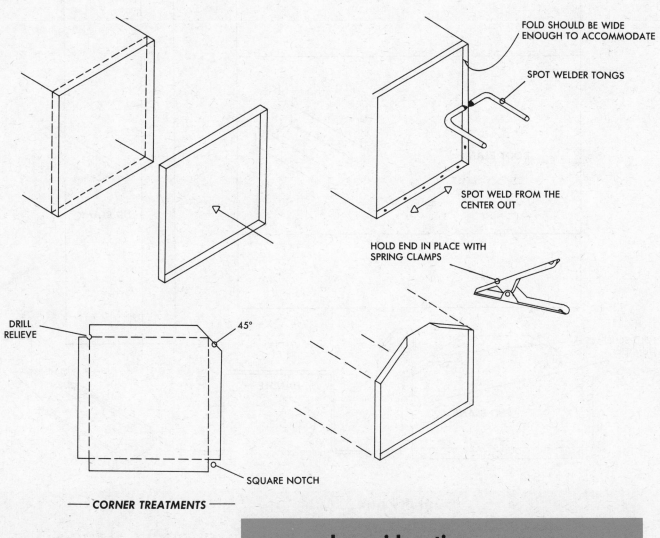

FOLD SHOULD BE WIDE
ENOUGH TO ACCOMMODATE

SPOT WELDER TONGS

SPOT WELD FROM THE
CENTER OUT

HOLD END IN PLACE WITH
SPRING CLAMPS

DRILL
RELIEVE

45°

SQUARE NOTCH

— CORNER TREATMENTS —

end considerations   utility box

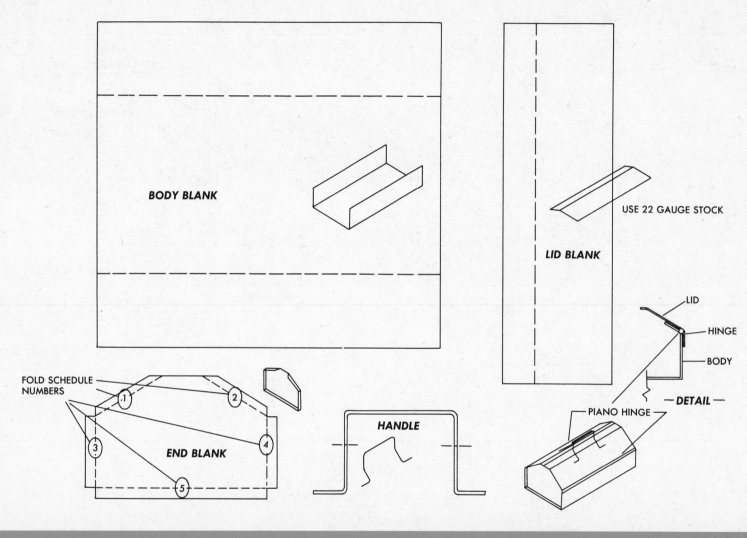

BODY BLANK

LID BLANK

USE 22 GAUGE STOCK

LID

HINGE

BODY

—DETAIL—

PIANO HINGE

FOLD SCHEDULE
NUMBERS

1   2

3   4

5

END BLANK

HANDLE

utility box

—sheet metal problem—

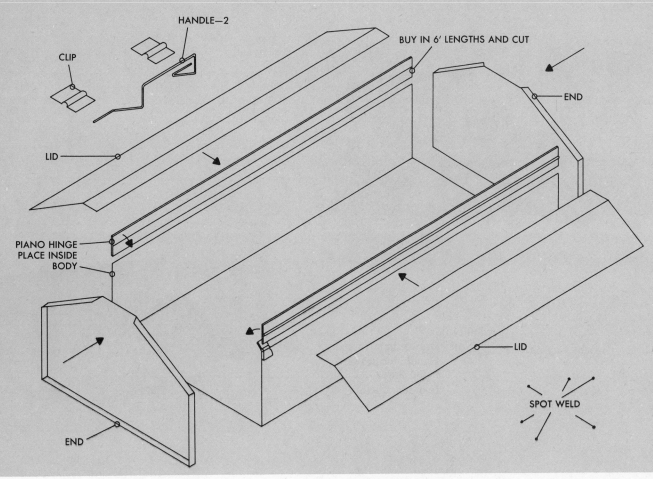

HANDLE—2

CLIP

BUY IN 6' LENGTHS AND CUT

END

LID

PIANO HINGE
PLACE INSIDE
BODY

LID

END

SPOT WELD

——— DETAIL UTILITY BOX ———

—— **sheet metal problem** ——

201

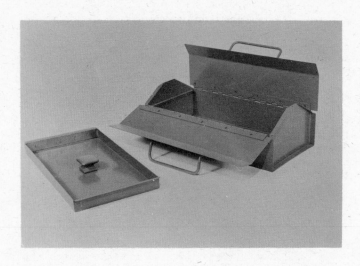

Utility Box
    Note: Drawer unit—metal
           Handle for drawer
           Piano hinge
           End construction

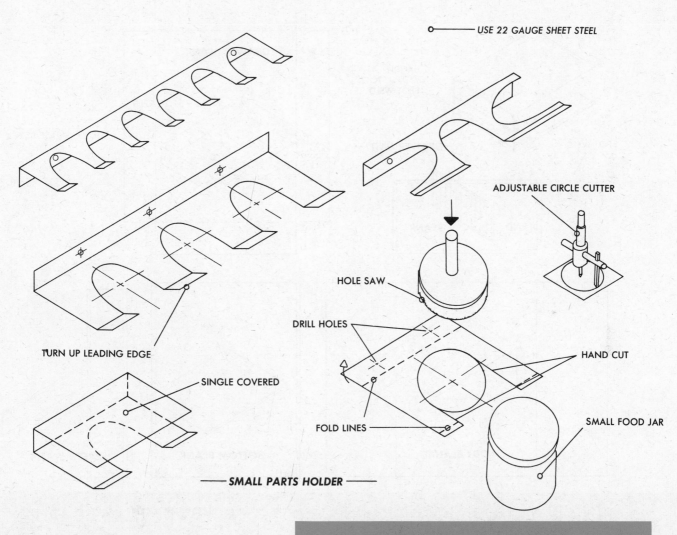

USE 22 GAUGE SHEET STEEL

ADJUSTABLE CIRCLE CUTTER

HOLE SAW

DRILL HOLES

HAND CUT

TURN UP LEADING EDGE

SINGLE COVERED

FOLD LINES

SMALL FOOD JAR

SMALL PARTS HOLDER

sheet metal problem

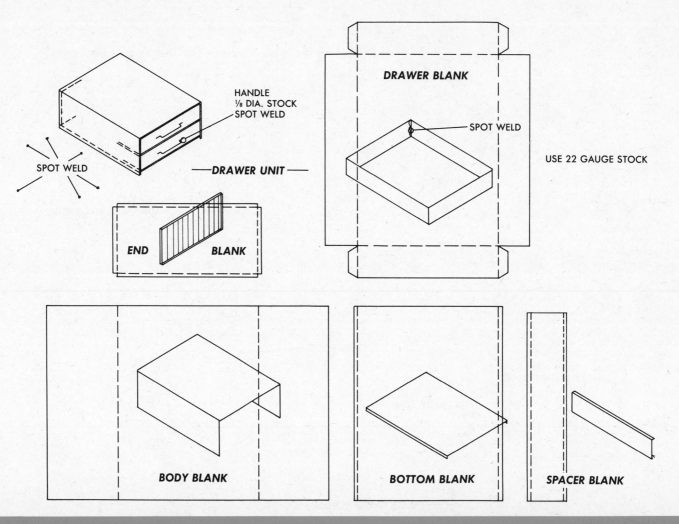

HANDLE
⅛ DIA. STOCK
SPOT WELD

DRAWER BLANK

SPOT WELD

SPOT WELD

—DRAWER UNIT—

USE 22 GAUGE STOCK

END   BLANK

BODY BLANK

BOTTOM BLANK

SPACER BLANK

drawer unit

sheet metal problem

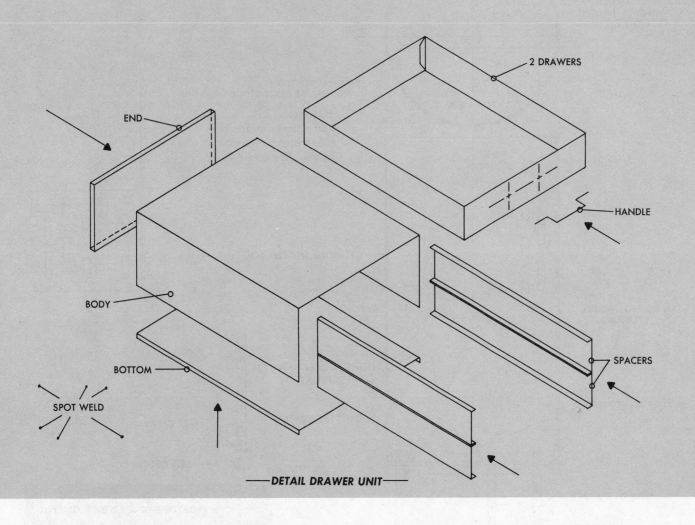

2 DRAWERS

END

HANDLE

BODY

SPACERS

BOTTOM

SPOT WELD

—— DETAIL DRAWER UNIT ——

—— **sheet metal problem** ——

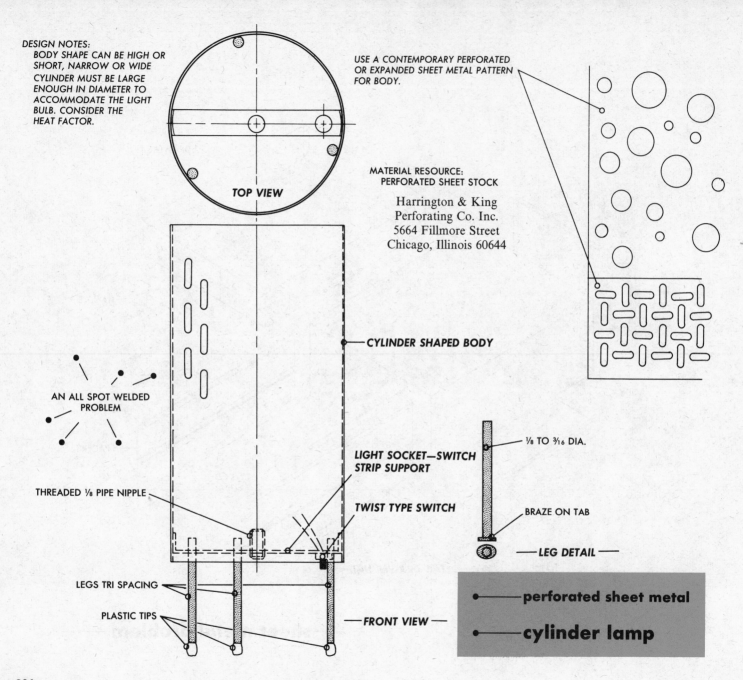

DESIGN NOTES:
BODY SHAPE CAN BE HIGH OR
SHORT, NARROW OR WIDE
CYLINDER MUST BE LARGE
ENOUGH IN DIAMETER TO
ACCOMMODATE THE LIGHT
BULB. CONSIDER THE
HEAT FACTOR.

USE A CONTEMPORARY PERFORATED
OR EXPANDED SHEET METAL PATTERN
FOR BODY.

TOP VIEW

MATERIAL RESOURCE:
PERFORATED SHEET STOCK

Harrington & King
Perforating Co. Inc.
5664 Fillmore Street
Chicago, Illinois 60644

CYLINDER SHAPED BODY

AN ALL SPOT WELDED
PROBLEM

**LIGHT SOCKET—SWITCH
STRIP SUPPORT**

THREADED ⅛ PIPE NIPPLE

TWIST TYPE SWITCH

⅛ TO ³⁄₁₆ DIA.

BRAZE ON TAB

— **LEG DETAIL** —

LEGS TRI SPACING

PLASTIC TIPS

— **FRONT VIEW** —

perforated sheet metal

cylinder lamp

206

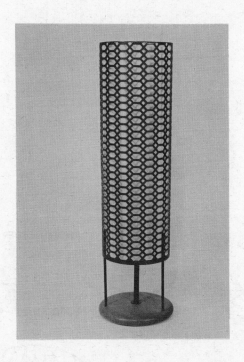

Cylinder Lamp
 Note: Expanded metal body
    Sculptured turned base

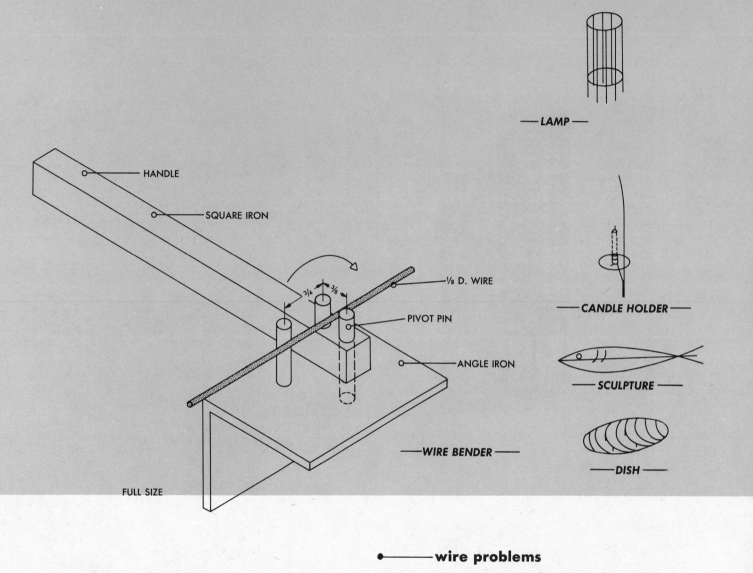

HANDLE

SQUARE IRON

⅛ D. WIRE

¾

⅜

PIVOT PIN

ANGLE IRON

WIRE BENDER

FULL SIZE

LAMP

CANDLE HOLDER

SCULPTURE

DISH

wire problems

spot welding problems

208

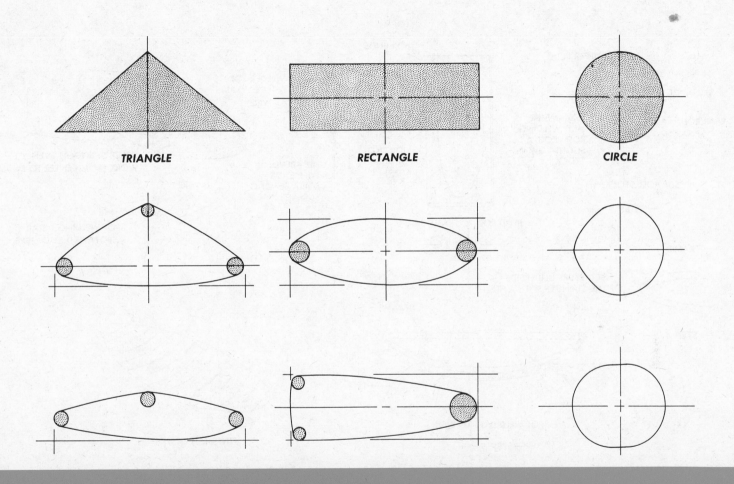

TRIANGLE   RECTANGLE   CIRCLE

THREE BASIC GEOMETRIC FORMS FROM WHICH WIRE
DISH SHAPE DESIGNS CAN EVOLVE: TRIANGLE,
RECTANGLE AND CIRCLE

●————wire dish shapes

209

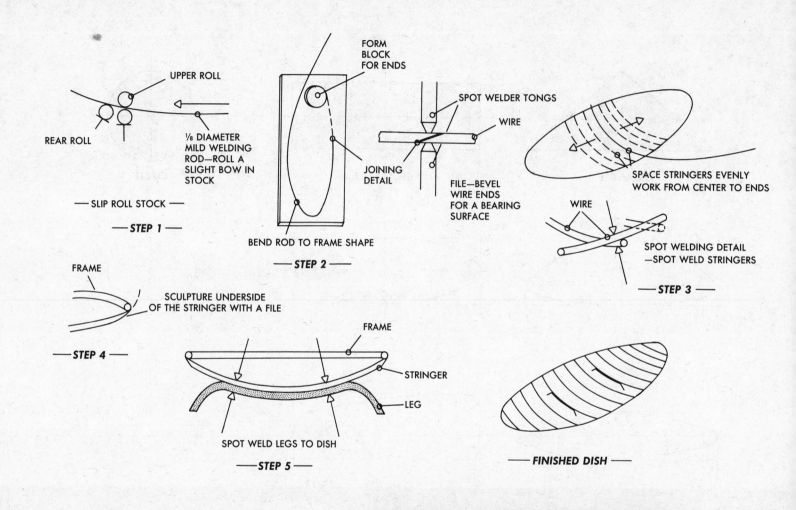

UPPER ROLL

REAR ROLL

⅛ DIAMETER MILD WELDING ROD—ROLL A SLIGHT BOW IN STOCK

— SLIP ROLL STOCK —

— STEP 1 —

FORM BLOCK FOR ENDS

JOINING DETAIL

BEND ROD TO FRAME SHAPE

— STEP 2 —

SPOT WELDER TONGS

WIRE

FILE—BEVEL WIRE ENDS FOR A BEARING SURFACE

SPACE STRINGERS EVENLY WORK FROM CENTER TO ENDS

WIRE

SPOT WELDING DETAIL —SPOT WELD STRINGERS

— STEP 3 —

FRAME

SCULPTURE UNDERSIDE OF THE STRINGER WITH A FILE

— STEP 4 —

FRAME

STRINGER

LEG

SPOT WELD LEGS TO DISH

— STEP 5 —

— FINISHED DISH —

construction considerations

wire dish

Wire Dish
  Note: Shape
        Spacing of runs
        Plastic leg tips
        One-piece legs

test the holding power of spot welds

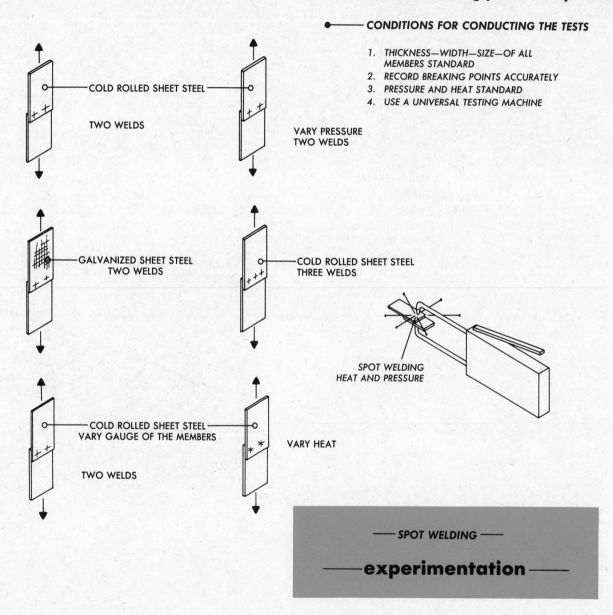

CONDITIONS FOR CONDUCTING THE TESTS

1. THICKNESS—WIDTH—SIZE—OF ALL MEMBERS STANDARD
2. RECORD BREAKING POINTS ACCURATELY
3. PRESSURE AND HEAT STANDARD
4. USE A UNIVERSAL TESTING MACHINE

COLD ROLLED SHEET STEEL

TWO WELDS

VARY PRESSURE
TWO WELDS

GALVANIZED SHEET STEEL
TWO WELDS

COLD ROLLED SHEET STEEL
THREE WELDS

SPOT WELDING
HEAT AND PRESSURE

COLD ROLLED SHEET STEEL
VARY GAUGE OF THE MEMBERS

TWO WELDS

VARY HEAT

— SPOT WELDING —

—experimentation—

CHAPTER 12

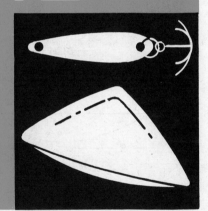

RAISING,
ENAMELING
AND SPINNING

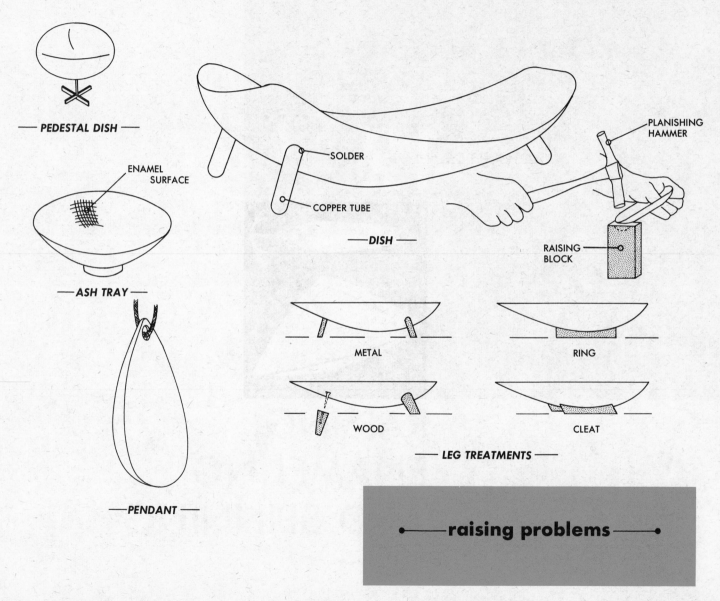

PEDESTAL DISH

ENAMEL
SURFACE

ASH TRAY

PENDANT

SOLDER

COPPER TUBE

DISH

PLANISHING
HAMMER

RAISING
BLOCK

METAL

RING

WOOD

CLEAT

LEG TREATMENTS

raising problems

problem: DESIGN A RAISED NONFERROUS DISH

LIMITATIONS OF PROBLEM:

Use a nonferrous metal
Dish shape must be a variation of a triangle

SUGGESTED MATERIAL:

18 Gauge nonferrous metal
—copper
—brass
—aluminum

TOTAL PROBLEM:

1. Full-size sketches of suggested shapes
2. Poster board template
3. Raised full-size prototype

PHYSICAL CONSIDERATIONS:

Materials limitation, cost, etc.
Physical properties of nonferrous materials
Raising limitations
Leg treatment
Finish
Tools and equipment available

DESIGN CONSIDERATIONS:

What will the dish hold? (function)
Legs—size, shape, material
Dish shape—variation of a triangle
Finish, satin, mirror
Should all raising marks be buffed out?
Type of liquid protection

MATERIALS:

18 Gauge, soft sheet copper, annealed stock
⅜ Diameter, 20-gauge copper tubing or walnut
   stock for legs

MATERIAL RESOURCE:

Nonferrous metal stock flat and tube

Brodhead-Garrett Co.
4560 E. 71st Street
Cleveland, Ohio 44105

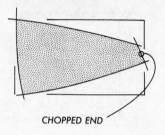

CHOPPED END

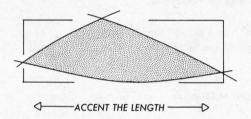

◁——— ACCENT THE LENGTH ———▷

•——— **VARIATION OF THE TRIANGLE** ———•

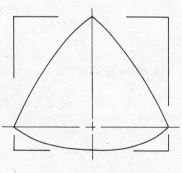

SEMI FORMAL SHAPE

POOR SHAPE ———

SCALENE TRIANGLE

SHIP CURVE FOR LINE
LAYOUT

•——— **raising dish designs**

•——— **shapes** ———•

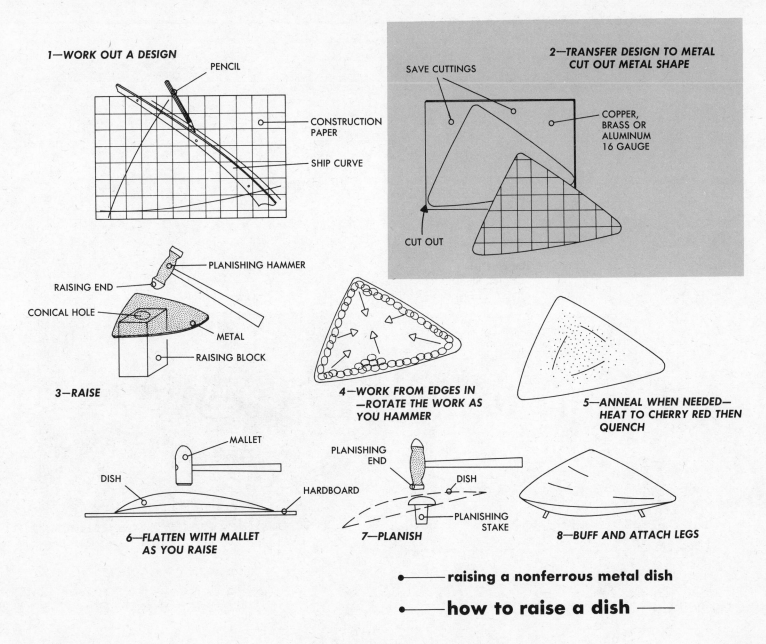

1—WORK OUT A DESIGN

PENCIL

CONSTRUCTION PAPER

SHIP CURVE

2—TRANSFER DESIGN TO METAL CUT OUT METAL SHAPE

SAVE CUTTINGS

COPPER, BRASS OR ALUMINUM 16 GAUGE

CUT OUT

PLANISHING HAMMER

RAISING END

CONICAL HOLE

METAL

RAISING BLOCK

3—RAISE

4—WORK FROM EDGES IN —ROTATE THE WORK AS YOU HAMMER

5—ANNEAL WHEN NEEDED— HEAT TO CHERRY RED THEN QUENCH

MALLET

DISH

HARDBOARD

6—FLATTEN WITH MALLET AS YOU RAISE

PLANISHING END

DISH

PLANISHING STAKE

7—PLANISH

8—BUFF AND ATTACH LEGS

• **raising a nonferrous metal dish**

• **how to raise a dish**

217

Raised Dish
Note: Shape
Legs

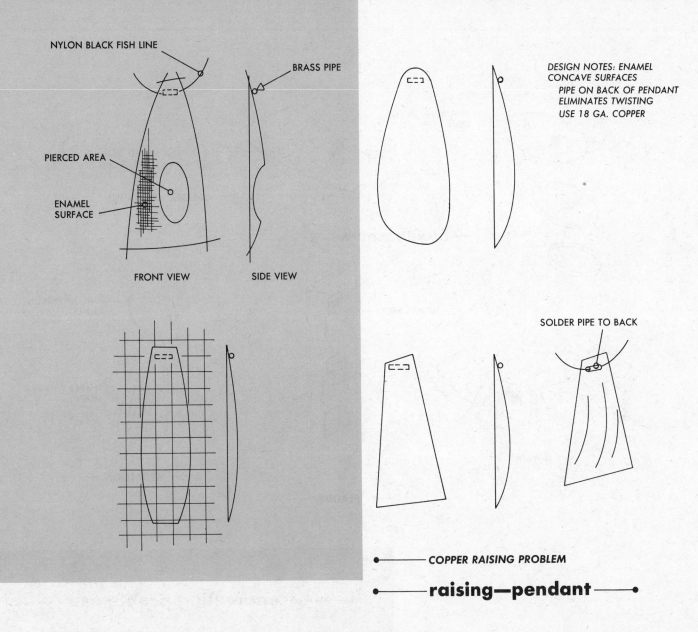

NYLON BLACK FISH LINE

BRASS PIPE

PIERCED AREA

ENAMEL SURFACE

FRONT VIEW

SIDE VIEW

DESIGN NOTES: ENAMEL
CONCAVE SURFACES
PIPE ON BACK OF PENDANT
ELIMINATES TWISTING
USE 18 GA. COPPER

SOLDER PIPE TO BACK

COPPER RAISING PROBLEM

raising—pendant

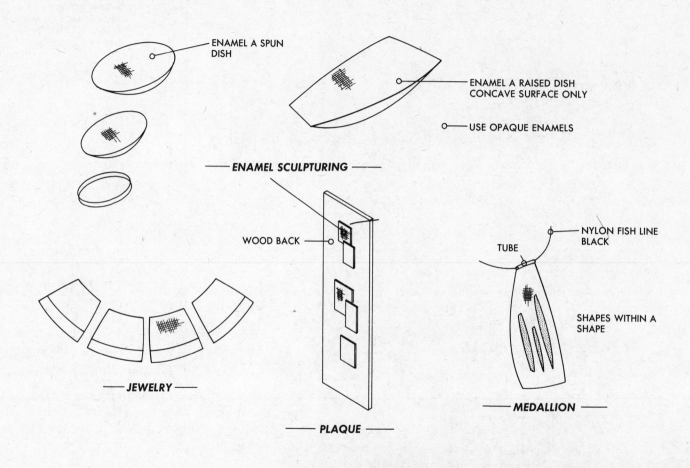

ENAMEL A SPUN
DISH

ENAMEL A RAISED DISH
CONCAVE SURFACE ONLY

USE OPAQUE ENAMELS

ENAMEL SCULPTURING

WOOD BACK

NYLON FISH LINE
BLACK

TUBE

SHAPES WITHIN A
SHAPE

JEWELRY

PLAQUE

MEDALLION

enameling problems

core problem: *ASH TRAY*

problem: *DESIGN AN ASH TRAY THAT WILL BE SPUN. THE CONCAVE SURFACE OF THE ASH TRAY WILL BE ENAMELED.*

LIMITATIONS OF PROBLEM:

Use a nonferrous metal (copper)
Ash tray must be spun

SUGGESTED MATERIALS:

22 Gauge nonferrous metal copper (soft)

TOTAL PROBLEM:

1. Full size sketches of suggested spinning forms (shape)
2. A two-view grid drawing of the spinning form
3. Turn form
4. Spin ash tray
5. Enamel concave surface of ash tray

MATERIAL RESOURCE: Copper

Brodhead-Garrett Co.
4560 E. 71st Street
Cleveland, Ohio 44105

PHYSICAL CONSIDERATIONS:

Physical properties of copper
Spinning limitations
Enameling limitations
Cost

DESIGN CONSIDERATIONS:

Function
Size
Shape— symmetrical
Finish— enamel surface, copper surface
Color— enamel, copper
Texture— enamel, copper

MATERIALS:

22 Gauge, soft sheet copper, annealed stock
Dry enamel

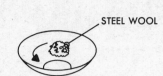

STEP 1. CLEANING

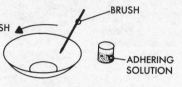

STEP 2. PROTECTOR

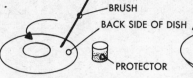

STEP 3. ADHERING SOLUTION

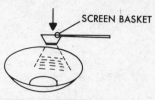

STEP 4. DRY ENAMEL

how to enamel

It is important to use care in the processes involved and to understand the reasons for each step. Enameling is not difficult. Give careful attention to such details as cleaning, application and firing, and you should have excellent results.

THE SIX BASIC STEPS

1. The first operation is to clean the spun copper dish. This should be done carefully and thoroughly if the enamel is to fuse completely with the metal. Clean both sides of the dish. Keep fingers or any greasy substance away from the surfaces of the copper. STEEL WOOL—ACID—WATER

2. Apply protector to the back of dish to prevent fire scale. Brush it on and allow it to dry before firing. If applied properly, protector will scale off when fired piece cools. PROTECTOR SOLUTION

3. Apply adhering solution to the concave surface of the dish with a brush. ADHERING SOLUTION

4. Dust on dry enamel through an 80-mesh shaker over wet adhering solution surface. Completely cover in depth. DRY ENAMEL

5. The dish now should be placed in the preheated (1500°) kiln and fired until smooth. Don't over fire. The dish is then removed to an asbestos pad until cool.
FIRING

6. Stone the lip of the dish. Buff the back side of the dish. Seal the back side of dish with a clear metal lacquer. CLEAR METAL LACQUER

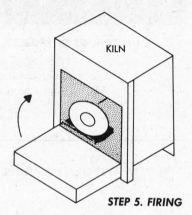

STEP 5. FIRING

RESOURCE

American Art Clay Company
4717 West Sixteenth Street
Indianapolis 24, Indiana

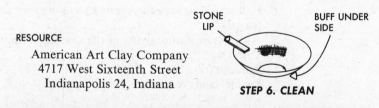

STEP 6. CLEAN

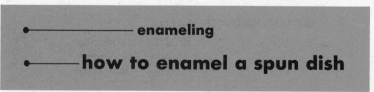

enameling

how to enamel a spun dish

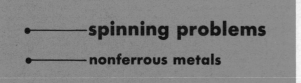
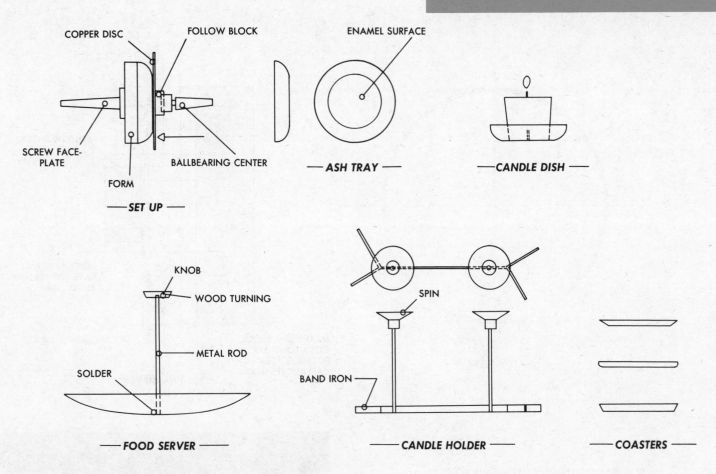

COPPER DISC   FOLLOW BLOCK   ENAMEL SURFACE

SCREW FACE-PLATE

FORM

BALLBEARING CENTER

—SET UP—

—ASH TRAY—

—CANDLE DISH—

KNOB

WOOD TURNING

METAL ROD

SOLDER

—FOOD SERVER—

SPIN

BAND IRON

—CANDLE HOLDER—

—COASTERS—

223

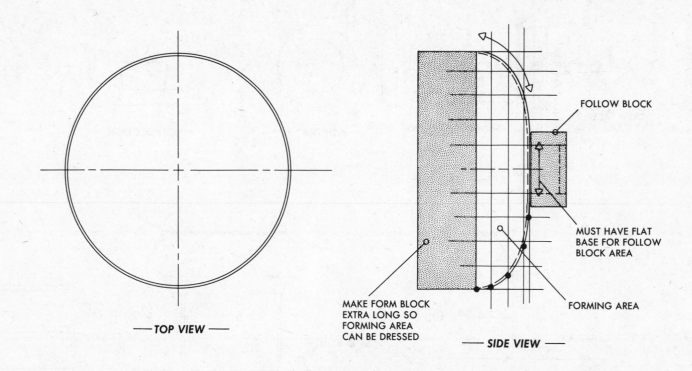

GRADUAL CURVED SURFACE
BEST FOR ENAMELING

ENAMEL WILL NOT RUN

FOLLOW BLOCK

MUST HAVE FLAT
BASE FOR FOLLOW
BLOCK AREA

FORMING AREA

MAKE FORM BLOCK
EXTRA LONG SO
FORMING AREA
CAN BE DRESSED

— SIDE VIEW —

— TOP VIEW —

DESIGN NOTE:—ENAMEL CONCAVE SURFACE FOR
UTILITY, COLOR AND TEXTURE
—DO NOT USE THREADS OR LUMPS
—DO MONOGRAMS OR SWIRLING

grid drawing

chuck form ash tray

224

Candle Holder
    Note: Spun candle holder dish
          Wood sculptured base

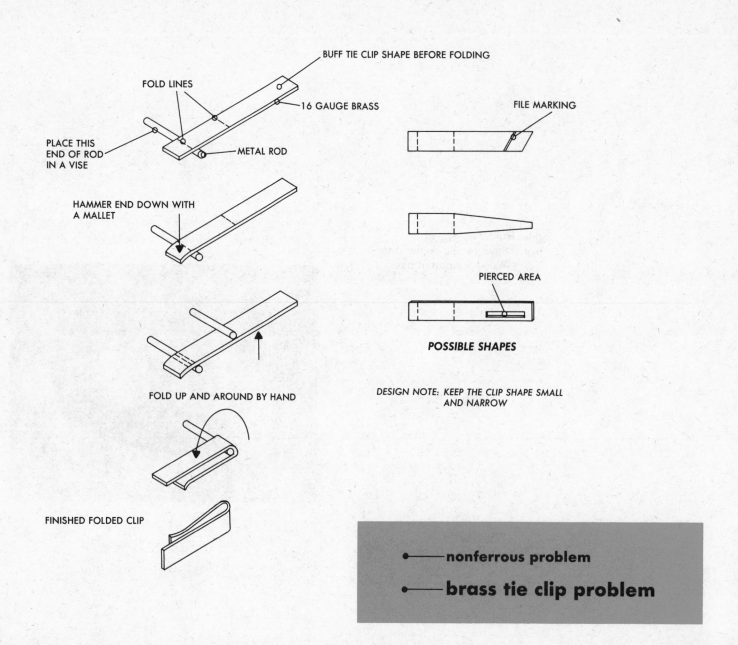

BUFF TIE CLIP SHAPE BEFORE FOLDING

FOLD LINES

16 GAUGE BRASS

PLACE THIS
END OF ROD
IN A VISE

METAL ROD

FILE MARKING

HAMMER END DOWN WITH
A MALLET

PIERCED AREA

POSSIBLE SHAPES

FOLD UP AND AROUND BY HAND

*DESIGN NOTE: KEEP THE CLIP SHAPE SMALL
AND NARROW*

FINISHED FOLDED CLIP

•——— **nonferrous problem**

•——— **brass tie clip problem**

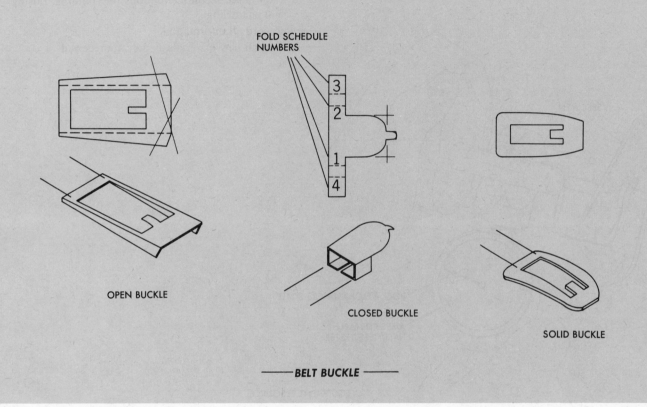

FOLD SCHEDULE
NUMBERS

3
2
1
4

OPEN BUCKLE

CLOSED BUCKLE

SOLID BUCKLE

BELT BUCKLE

sheet metal layout

a problem in brass

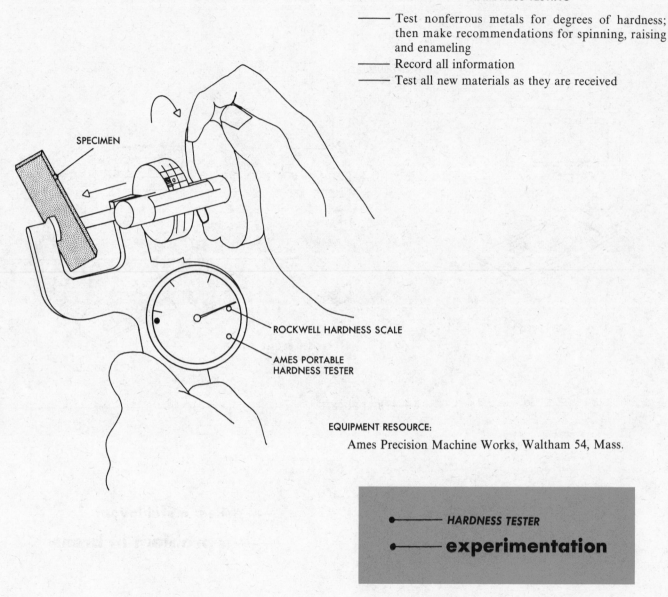

SPECIMEN

ROCKWELL HARDNESS SCALE

AMES PORTABLE
HARDNESS TESTER

—— Test nonferrous metals for degrees of hardness; then make recommendations for spinning, raising and enameling

—— Record all information

—— Test all new materials as they are received

EQUIPMENT RESOURCE:

Ames Precision Machine Works, Waltham 54, Mass.

● ——— *HARDNESS TESTER*

● ——— **experimentation**